D1369399

Musée des Thermes
et de l'Hôtel de Cluny

6, place Paul-Painlevé
75005 Paris
Tél. : 43 25 62 00

Musée de Cluny
guide

by
Alain Erlande-Brandenburg
Conservateur en chef du Musée de Cluny

and Jean-Pierre Caillet
Fabienne Joubert
Elisabeth Taburet-Delahaye
Conservateurs au Musée de Cluny

*Ministère de la Culture
et de la Communication*

*Editions
de la Réunion des Musées Nationaux*

Paris 1987

Translation:
Jean-Marie Clarke

Cover: Altarpiece
of the Lamentation
of Christ (detail)

© Editions de la Réunion
des Musées Nationaux
Paris 1987
10, Rue de l'Abbaye
75006 Paris

ISBN (French edition, RMN, 1986)
2-7118-2.070-X
ISBN (English edition, RMN)
2-7118-2.071-8

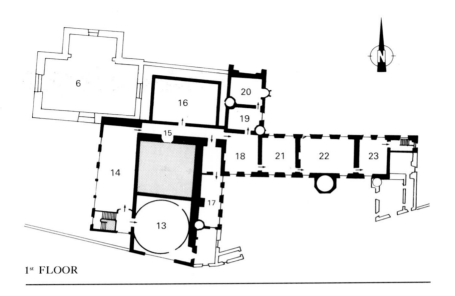

1st FLOOR

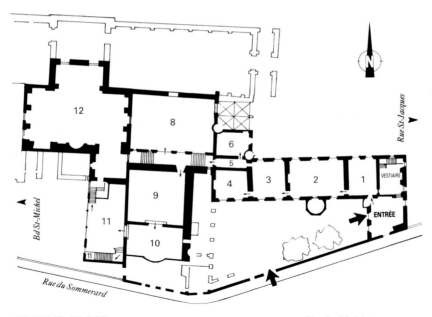

GROUND FLOOR

Place Paul-Painlevé

Thermae
- *The Frigidarium*
- *Floor-plan*

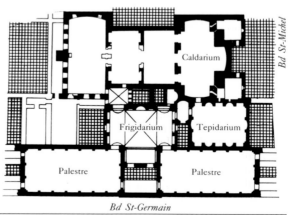

Caldarium

Frigidarium

Tepidarium

Palestre

Palestre

Bd St-Michel

Bd St-Germain

The "Musée de Cluny"

The Musée de Cluny and the Musée des Thermes have the rare merit of being situated in buildings that are in complete harmony with the collections which they house. This association was the result not of chance, but of an intention which took almost a century to realize. Indeed, what better place to exhibit the great vestiges of ancient Paris than the Gallo-Roman baths *(thermae)*, and what more perfect setting than the Gothic *hôtel* of the Abbots of Cluny for one of the richest collections of Medieval art in the world. It was with the re-organization of the museum after the Second World War that this harmonious ensemble was finally brought to completion.

The buildings

The Baths

The Gallo-Roman *Thermae* are one of the most impressive monuments left by the ancient occupants of Lutetia, as Paris was then called. At the time it was divided into two agglomerations: the first, nestled on the Ile de la Cité, was surrounded by a protective wall in the 3rd century; and the second, established by the Roman conquerors on the Montagne Sainte-Geneviève, was grouped on the hillside running down to the Seine. Between them were the great river and also marshes which extended to the present-day boulevard Saint-Germain. In Antiquity, the public buildings were located towards the south: the forum under the present-day rue Soufflot, near the southern baths; the eastern baths on the site of the Collège de France, and the northern baths at the intersection of the boulevards Saint-Germain and Saint-Michel.

The building here was constructed on a platform of beaten earth to the South, and over a cellar on the North side to compensate for the slope of the terrain. The architect designed it according to a rectangular plan of dimensions (100 m × 65 m) similar to those of the *Thermae* of Cherchel, in Algeria, but far from the scale of those at Trier (170 m × 100 m). Excavations carried out in the 19th century under the careful supervision of Théodore Vacquer and then after the Second World War by Paul-Marie Duval have made it possible to reconstitute the original floor-plan and disposition of the three rooms: the *Frigidarium*, which is entirely intact, the *Tepidarium*, and the *Caldarium*, both in ruins, all of which were interconnected in a fixed order. There was another room—today occupied by rooms IX and X of the museum—

which was heated and probably served as a meeting room. The palaestras (gymnasiums) were to the East and West, on either side of the *Frigidarium*. Built all in one piece of small stone blocks separated by courses of tie-bricks, the building dates from the last quarter of the 2nd century or the first quarter of the next century. The pattern of brick and stone whose quality, regularity, and colors are so attractive today, used to be hidden under various types of covering. The presence, under the spring of the arches of the *Frigidarium*, of corbels in the shape of ship's prows laden with arms would seem to indicate that the construction was financed by the powerful corporation of the Paris boatmen, the *Nautes*.

The house of the abbots of Cluny

It was in this part of the city, abandoned in the wake of the barbarian invasions, that the University established itself, thus forming what came to be called the Latin Quarter. The powerful abbots of Cluny acquired several houses next to the baths, along with rights to the hanging gardens above the ancient vaults, and made this their residence when they came on visits from Burgundy. At the end of the 15th century, the abbot Jacques d'Amboise (1485-1510), whose brothers distinguished themselves by their generosity as patrons of the arts, had a house built that was more in keeping with his taste for luxury and which soon came to be known as the "Amboise Palace". It was built on a U-shaped plan, with a main wing to the North, flanked by two smaller side wings connected to the South by a crenelated wall that once had a sentry-walk. On the South side, therefore, was created a protected courtyard. Extending on the North side is another wing which housed the chapel and a large room. This was one of the first examples of a type of house—"between courtyard and garden"—that was to become very popular during the 17th century in Paris and in the major provincial cities.

Hôtel de Cluny
- *Vault of the Chapel*
- *The courtyard*

The objects in the museum's collections have a variety of provenances, but three sources are of particular importance, for they gave the museum its special character: the collection of Alexandre Du Sommerad, the stonework deposit of the City of Paris, and the acquisitions made after the creation of the museum. At present, over 23,000 objects have been inventoried.

Alexandre Du Sommerard

Born in 1771, at Bar-sur-Aube, Alexandre Du Sommerard opted very early for the military life, then joined the staff of the Cour des Comptes (State Audit Office) as Chief Clerk in 1807, moving up to the position of Principal Adviser by the end of his career. At a time when an inordinate taste for Antiquity held sway and the Medieval and Renaissance periods were little appreciated, not to say disdained, he developed a keen interest in just these periods. Du Sommerard soon established himself as a precursor in this specialty, and his curiosity extended to many other fields. To illustrate a large work on the "Arts of the Middle Ages"—five volumes published between 1838 and 1846—he made use of lithography, a process that was still in its infancy, but which permitted him to reproduce a large number of objects in his collection, as well as in others. Following the example of the so-called "antiquarians", Debruge-Dumenil, Revoil, Sauvageot, and many others, he set about acquiring objects, some of which have since proved to be great masterpieces. In order to finance his purchases, he had to sell a fine collection of drawings by old and modern masters in 1826. His collection soon became famous among Parisians, for he liked to move around in Society and in literary circles, and he was free in his invitations to visitors. An 1825 painting by Xavier Leprince titled *The Antiquarian* portrays Du Sommerard in his home, then in the rue Ménars, surrounded by many precious objects.

Their growing number soon obliged him to move, and his choice—which proved to be an excellent one—went to the house of the Cluny abbots. Like Alexandre Lenoir, who had previously founded the Musée des Monuments Français in the convent of the Petits-Augustins, he was imaginative enough to take advantage of the setting and to show his treasures in a decor designed to strike the sensitivity of his visitors. Contemporary engravings and paintings give us an idea of the care which he took in their display. With an amazing sense of theatre, he succeeded in evoking the memory of great figures from the past. François I, whom Sauvageot liked to refer to as "my king", was especially favored: an entire room was devoted to him, containing his bed, his stirrups, and a host of other objects generously attributed to him. Otherwise, there was a fantastic mixture of techniques and periods, with the most varied objects being juxtaposed in complete defiance of chronology, most of them associated with some illustrious origin. Fakes invariably made their way into this tremendous array of bric-à-brac, for methods of authentication at the time were a far cry from what they are today, and so gullible buyers were an easy prey for clever forgers.

Du Sommerard's contemporaries, aware of the relationship that had been established between this collection and the building in which it was housed, expressed the desire that this association become permanent through the creation of a museum. At the Salon of 1833, Albert Lenoir, the son of the founder of the Musée des Monuments Français, presented a "Project for a historical museum formed by the joining of the Palais des Thermes and the Hôtel de Cluny". This idea was greeted with enthusiastic acclaim, all the more so because the City of Paris had set up a stonework deposit in the *Frigidarium* of the baths.

The city stonework deposit

The Gallo-Roman baths, which had been proclaimed national property during the Revolution, did not find a buyer, and so they were turned over to the hospice of Charenton in 1809. Even before then, however, concern for their preservation and use had been expressed by the "*antiquomanes*", or enthusiasts of Antiquity. Baltard, in 1807, had suggested that the *Frigidarium* be emptied and used for the placement of "sculptures executed in Paris or at least brought there by the Romans". In 1809, Grivaud again took up the idea of the creation of a museum, followed by Quatremère de Quincy in 1817. The closing, in 1816, of the Musée des Monuments Français created during the Revolution by Alexandre Lenoir was to reinforce this trend in public opinion, whose principal argument was the need to protect the sculptures that had been housed there. Alexandre Lenoir, hoping to see his old museum resurrected, was himself an earnest advocate of this idea. In 1819, responding to this movement, Louis XVIII ordered the ruins to be purchased, the *Thermae* to be cleared, and appointed a curator who saw to the placing of the ancient sculptures. The State very quickly lost interest in the matter, however, and the City of Paris took things over in 1836. In imitation of the other great cities of the realm, Paris felt the need to have its own "museum of Gallic and Roman antiquities". It immediately set about depositing sculptures that came from demolitions, the restoration of Parisian buildings, and even from excavations. The efforts put into this undertaking were not unrelated to the hope that the Du Sommerard collection next door would soon become national property.

The death of Alexandre Du Sommerard on August 19, 1842, was to accelerate this process. Through astute negotiations, the City offered to turn the *Thermae* and the stonework collection over to the State on the condition that Edmond, the son of the famous collector, be appointed curator. On July 1st of the following year, the Chambre des Députés voted for the purchase of the house and of the collections. The law of July 24, 1843 officially ratified the creation of the "Musée des Thermes et de l'Hôtel de Cluny"; its curator was Edmond Du Sommerard, and its architect Albert Lenoir. During the lengthy debates that preceded this decision, the former Musée des Monuments Français was frequently evoked. Its memory hovered over the proceedings like a phantom presence to which it was hoped that new substance could be given; there was also much regret, for its closing had caused considerable emotion.

The opening of the new museum was a triumph. On March 17, 1844 the number of visitors reached 12,000, and on the following Sunday, 16,000. The merger of these two collections of widely differing origins was to give the museum a character which it still retains today, one of an extraordinary variety. The City's contribution consisted of the capitals of Saint-Germain-des-Prés, the statues from Notre-Dame discovered in 1839 in the rue de la Santé, as well as the ancient fragments that were formerly in the Musée des Monuments Français: the blocks of the Pillar of the Nautes, the bull of Saint-Marcel. The second group of works consisted of the 1,434 objects of the Du Sommerard collection, and these were distributed among the 19 rooms then open. In addition to these marvels, the public had the opportunity to discover two superb monuments: the Gallo-Roman baths and the Medieval house of Jacques d'Amboise.

The appointment of Edmond Du Sommerard as head of this vast complex proved to have been a wise decision, for at his death in 1885, after a directorship of forty years, he left behind a catalogue totalling 10,351 items. It is he who should be considered as the true creator of the museum. His first task was to bring order into his father's collections; in his first catalogue published in 1847, he adopted a system of classification based on the different types of arts and crafts. Within each of these categories, objects were listed in chronological order; the collector had made way once and for all for the scientist. He then undertook he re-organization of the rooms, which until the Second World War would retain aspects reminiscent of their 19th-century origins, and also managed to set up the museum of national antiquities whose creation had so fervently been desired.

Operating under the authority of the Commission des Monuments Historiques, he was able to acquire a good number of architectural and sculptural fragments from restoration projects (the apostles from the Sainte-Chapelle) and demolitions (the chapel of the College of Cluny). The stonework collection was completed with plaster casts, thus forming a first version of the future museum of comparative sculpture, which has since been given the old name of Musée des Monuments Français. Edmond Du Sommerard extended the exhibition area to the garden that had been created at the behest of Napoleon III, setting up architectural and sculptural elements, and casts under the newly-planted trees. The famous Elysée Gardens of the former Musée des Monuments Français thus made a timid reappearance.

His untiring activity as a curator also included making purchases. Thus he kept a watchful eye on the antiques market, losing no opportunity to enrich the museum, and he is responsible for the acquisition of some of its greatest masterpieces. In Rouen, he bought the six tapestries of *La Vie Seigneuriale*, after having acquired in Genoa the ten Brussels hangings of the *History of David* series (today in the

● *The Lady with the Unicorn*
Smell (detail)

● *The Lady with the Unicorn*
Sight (detail)

Musée de la Renaissance at Ecouen), which have no match for their size and beauty in any of the other museums of France. When the Hôtel-Dieu of Auxerre decided to sell the tapestries of the cathedral, he immediately persuaded the Commission and the ministry to acquire them for Cluny. It was also he who negotiated with the township of Boussac for the purchase of the marvellous series of *The Lady with the Unicorn*. As for gold and silverwork, he enriched the museum with several unique pieces: the gold crowns of the kings of the Visigoths, found by a French officer living in Spain; the fabulous remains of the treasury of the Cathedral of Basel, the altar given by Emperor Henry I, and the golden rose, put up for sale by the canton and bought by a private collector. His acquisitions in other domains were no less remarkable: six monumental sculpted fireplaces, three large ceramic medallions by the Della Robbias (today at Ecouen), enamelwork, and even a collection of illustrated lead medallions found in the Seine.

His successor, Alfred Darcel, concerned himself primarily with rectifying the collections, removing imitations, dismantling composite pieces of furniture, an initiative which Edmond had not dared to take, out of respect for his father's memory.

In 1907, the museum was detached from the Commission des Monuments Historiques and came under the authority of the Administration des Musées Nationaux. The directorship was given to Edmond Haraucourt, a poet and man of letters, whose principal accomplishment was to increase the number of objects in the catalogue by removing them from the places of storage to which they had been relegated.

After him, J.-J. Marquet de Vasselot undertook a vast campaign of re-organization, removing many objects that were out of place, and arranging displays that were more in keeping with the taste of his contemporaries.

The closing of the Musée de Cluny in 1939 marked the end of an era, that of the 19th-century institution whose life had spanned almost one hundred years. A new era was to begin with the end of the Second World War.

The works had been transferred to a safe place for the duration of the hostilities. With the return of peace, there was much architectural work to be done, and a new presentation of the collections had to be designed. It was recognized that the needs of the spectators, who had long suffered from the crowding of the displays into small spaces, had to be taken into account. It was therefore decided that ancient sculpture would be exhibited in the Gallo-Roman baths, and Medieval works in the 15th-century house.

The display of an amazing diversity of collections had to be adapted to buildings whose own qualities had to be respected. Thus the monumental room of the *Thermae*, the finest example of its kind on French soil, had to be presented for itself. So as not to detract from the great beauty of its space, the exhibits were limited to a few sculptures found in Paris and of the same period. The same applied to the chapel, a precious relic of the last stages of the Flamboyant style in the Gothic architecture of Paris. The collections themselves have been distributed among the twenty-four rooms.

The entrance to the collections leads through the former kitchen area of the Cluny house. The only remaining vestige is the magnificent stone fireplace whose mantel features a keystone with a representation of the Trinity; it was originally in the Convent of the Trinity in Jativa, Spain.

Room I

Costume

Because of its inherent fragility, little clothing has come down to us, and most of it has been found in tombs. To have an idea of what was worn, we have to rely on contemporary documents, such as manuscript illuminations, paintings, tapestries, or sculpture, taking into account the lapse of time between the appearance of a fashion and its representation in illustrations, and making allowances for the effects of artistic licence.

Shoes

Leather goods, on the other hand, less fragile and produced in great quantities during the Middle Ages, have been better preserved. Many shoes have been found in tombs, some of them in remarkably good condition. During construction between 1923 and 1927 on the site of the present-day church of Notre-Dame de Bonne-Nouvelle in Paris, were unearthed a shoe for the right foot and the upper of a shoe for the left foot, as well as a buckle, displayed in the showcase to the right of the door; they probably date from the 14th or 15th centuries.

To the left of this door, another showcase presents the soles of a right foot and a left foot, with very pointed tips in the late 14th-century style, as well as a soft leather upper decorated with openwork lozenges with toothed edges; all three come from the same excavation. The boot sole, of a later date because of its square toe, was found in the tomb of King Alfonso V (†1458), at the convent of El Cobret in Spain. The man's shoe with a rounded toe in the so-called "bear's foot" fashion is from the late 15th century; many examples it are to be seen in contemporary illuminations and tapestries.

Costume accessories

There was a great diversity of costumes accessories during the Middle Ages, as can be seen by the display in this showcase. Most of the pieces come from the collection assembled by Victor Gay during his lifetime and afterwards bequeathed to the museum. A variety of materials was used to make these ornamental objects (lead being the cheapest) in the form of letters, fleur-de-lys, and even alms-purses, which were then sewn onto clothing. The same went for studs. Others, such as purse mounts, belt pendants and fittings, small chains, buckles, and book clasps, were cast in bronze. The craftsmen liked to decorate them with finely-wrought motifs, like this Annunciation on a circular pendant.

Caskets

Caskets, cases, and book-covers were as varied as the types of material of which they were made. Some were made of metal (see Room XXII), while others, such as the three caskets and single case here, were made of leather. One of the caskets has metal mounts (1), another has a domed lid, and the third, which also has a domed lid, features embossed scenes, one of which depicts a unicorn hunt (2). The bookcover has an elegant chased decoration.

Showcase 3

One of the caskets features the repeated motif of a couple, while the inside of the lid presents an engraved Virgin and Child. There is a fine goblet case with an unidentified coat-of-arms. The case shaped like a saddle-holster, with seven compartments and the embossed decoration of a Nativity and four saints, has a lid stamped with the royal coat-of-arms, while the back bears the arms of the city of Dijon.

Showcase 4

The forms of these objects are as diverse as their origins. The long casket with a domed lid and embossed animal motifs is a 14th-century Spanish work; while the small house-shaped chest with engraved scenes from literature and from the Life of Christ, as well as the casket bearing the engraved initials "MC" on the lid, are of 14th-century Italian execution.

Wood

The large wooden chest, a stable chest that must have been used to contain oats for horses, is just as unusual by its size as by its decor of applied arcades, and probably dates from the 1300's. In the middle of the room stands an extraordinary pillar surmounted by an angel bearing the coat-of-arms of Philippe Bouton, the prior of Saint-Pierre-le-Moûtier (Nièvre) between 1490 and 1510; it is said to have come from the chapter room. Above the doorway to the next room is a wonderful Annunciation carved in fine walnut, the work of an early 16th-century German artist.

1-2. Caskets

1

2

Tapestry

The Musée de Cluny can pride itself on having one of the richest collections of Medieval tapestry in the world. Contemporary documents tell us of the extraordinary richness of this production, but very little of it has survived intact.

On the East wall hangs an early 16th-century tapestry illustrating the then popular Medieval legend of the Sybil of Tibur, who, upon being questioned by the Emperor Augustus as to who would rule the Empire after him, indicated the Virgin and Child (3). On the South wall, the *Concert* evokes the more pleasant aspects of feudal life, representations of which were much sought after.

3. Augustus and the Sybil

Room II

1

Tapestry

This room is devoted especially to tapestries, some of which date back to the first third of the 15th century, while others are from the 1500's.

1. The Offering of the Heart

The *Offering of the Heart* (1) is, along with *The Resurrection* (Room III), one of the museum's earliest hangings. Woven in wool, it represents a man literally offering his heart to a woman seated in verdant surroundings set against a dark-blue ground. The elegance of the figures and the freely-flowing costumes are in keeping with the International Gothic style of the 1400's, of which this work is one of the last manifestations.

The *Deliverance of St. Peter* (2) comes from a large series donated to the Cathedral of Beauvais in 1460 by its bishop, Guillaume de Hellande. It features the arms of the cathedral chapter and those of the donor, as well as his motto: *Pax*. The other tapestries of this set are in Beauvais, in museums in America, and in private collections. The drapery is characterized by the same flowing lines as above, unlike the style developed a few years later which adopted more angular folds.

The *Miracle of St. Quentin* is a choir hanging that comes from the basilica of Saint-Quentin in the North of France. It depicts the episodes of a miracle by this saint, as related below, almost in comic-strip fashion, in a long poem written in the dialect of Picardy.

2. The Delivrance of St. Peter

The Grape Harvest
3. Complete
4. Detail

3

The *Grape Harvest* (3-4) represents scenes that are closer to everyday life: on the right, the picking, and on the left, the pressing of the grapes. A third scene, on the far right, has unfortunately been cut away. The coats-of-arms of the owner and of his wife, who have yet to be identified, were sewn into the corners at the top.

The function of the folding "table" displayed in the middle of the room—if it was indeed a table—remains a mystery. It may have been designed as a sort of profane "altarpiece" with panels

4

that could alternately be opened and closed. The painting is the work of a mid-14th-century German artist, and it has come down to us in an excellent state of preservation. The shields and inscriptions on the border refer to the principal provinces and towns of the Holy Roman Empire. At the center, alternating with shields topped by plumed helmets, are four quatrefoils framing scenes that are difficult to interpret: from left to right, the story of the *Golden Ass* of Apuleus, an Oriental proverb (the paths of the bird's flight through the air, of the serpent on the ground, of the ship on the sea, and of youth, cannot be apprehended by the mind), the legend of *Barlaam and Jehoshaphat* (?), and the *Judgment of Solomon*.

The altarpiece from the church of Champdeuil (Seine-et-Marne) illustrates the Life of Christ. The style indicates a date around the first third of the 16th century and identifies it as the work of a local artist who based himself on an altarpiece in the Antwerp style. The side panels are signed Lucas Loïs and are of Parisian origin.

5. *Head of the funeral effigy of of Jeanne de Toulouse*

Sculpture

Displayed between the windows is the very lovely head of the *gisante* (recumbent funeral effigy) of Jeanne de Toulouse (5), the wife of Alphonse de Poitiers, the brother of Saint Louis; she died in 1271 while returning from the crusade to Tunis. In 1280, Philip the Bold commissioned a Parisian artist to execute an effigy to be placed in the abbey church of Gercy (Essonne); this head is all that remains.

Another statue shows a peasant of the early 1500's, with the typical costume and attributes of his condition: staff, mantle, pouch, cask, etc.

Room III

2

Weavers and Embroiderers

One of the most active trades in the Middle Ages, along with that of precious metalwork, was that of fine textiles. Although we know for a fact that Byzantine silk of the Carolingian period and Italian silk of the 15th century were in great demand, that the drapers occupied a very important position in the great fairs of Champagne, and that the wool merchants brought enormous riches to the cities of Flanders, it is much more difficult to determine the exact origin and place of manufacture of many of the specimens of textiles that have come down to us.

1. Bust-reliquary
of St. Mabilla
2. Life and Miracles
of St. Martin

French embroiderers, however, were far from being the leaders in their craft during the Middle Ages: work of English make, known as *opus anglicanum*, became synonymous with the high quality of embroidery that was the most sought-after.

On the wall opposite the entrance there is a poignant bust-reliquary (Italian, 15th century) which contains the skull of St. Mabilla, one of the Eleven Thousand Virgins who were martyred in Cologne (1). Carved in wood, it still presents traces of the delicate colors with which it was painted. On either side are two large embroidered panels: one is from the 13th century (Iceland) and depicts the life and miracles of St. Martin (2); the composition in

3

medallions shows the influence of French stained-glass windows; the other is from the lst half of the 15th century; this fine altar-cloth (Gift of Baron Adolphe de Rothschild, 1889), features episodes from the lives of St. Mark and of St. John framed by canopies set against a yellow background highlighted with silver (3).

Ivories

Showcase 1. In the middle of the room.

This showcase displays most of the museum's collection of Gothic ivories.

In the *upper sections* are caskets of different sizes and from very different periods. The largest one, in the center, features episodes from the Life of Christ and from the story of Job. The exquisite mirror-case lid representing a royal couple was fashioned from an exceptionally thick plaque in Paris around 1300 (4).

3. Scenes from the Life
of St. Mark
and the Life of St. John
4. Royal couple

Panel 1 displays pieces from the second half of the 13th and the early 14th century. The diptych fragment decorated with scenes from the Passion and placed in the middle (5) belongs to a group of works whose style is closely related to monumental sculpture of the years 1250-1260; this group of works, formed around a diptych from the church of Saint-Jean-des-Vignes in Soissons, is attributed to the "workshop of the Soissons diptych".

4

Panel 2 presents both ecclesiastical and secular works of the 14th century; these diptychs and panels usually decorated with scenes of the Life of Christ, mirror-case lids, writing tablets and plaquettes depicting courting couples, tournament scenes, and episodes from literature, demonstrate the importance and the diversity of ivory carving at this time.

The plaquettes displayed on *Panel 3* date from the second half of the 14th or the beginning of the 15th century. The four polyptych panels representing scenes from the lives of Saints Peter and Paul (6) have been attributed to a Parisian workshop active during the 3rd quarter of the 14th century. The *Crucifixion* (7) placed below is related, however, to a group of ivories associated with a diptych kept in the Abbey of Kremsmünster (Austria) which were probably executed in the Rhineland in the early 15th century.

The activity of the ivory workshops continued during the 15th century, as can be seen by the casket plaques executed in shallow relief illustrating episodes from the Life of Christ, displayed on *Panel 4*.

5. *Scenes of the Passion of Christ*
6. *Scenes
from the Life of St Paul*
7. *Crucifixion*

5

6

7

Textiles

Showcase and Panel 2 between the windows on the garden side.

The Marcel Guérin bequest enriched the Musée de Cluny with a collection of textiles assembled by this discerning collector. They have been grouped in a showcase with many drawers, but only the textiles of Coptic origin (8), i.e. woven in Egypt between the 4th and 10th centuries of the Christian era and found in tombs, are displayed on the wall and above the showcase. The principal interest of these small tapestries is their bright colors (the piece with the bird motif) and their vigorous designs (the lion).

8. *Coptic textile*
9. *Quadriga*

Showcase and Panel 3 to the right of the window overlooking the garden.

The Court of Byzantium, at the gates of the Orient, provided the silk weavers with a tremendous amount of activity. Some of the most splendid textiles ever made came from the Imperial workshops. All during the first centuries of the Middle Ages, there was never any question of their superiority in the Western world. Many of these textiles were found in tombs or reliquaries, and nearly all in a fragmentary state. It is very rare indeed to discover, as did some years ago the clergy ot the Cathedral of Rheims in conjunction with the Monuments Historiques, a shroud as well-preserved as that of Saint Rémi.

8

9

Displayed are a number of very fine
specimens, such as the large piece of
blue fabric decorated with a quadriga
(four-horse chariot) that belonged to
the treasury of Aix-la-Chapelle
(Aachen) (9), or the splendid fragment
with a red blackground which features
the repeated motif of Samson opening
the jaws of a lion, or again the small
piece representing Amazons. All three
were woven in Byzantium or in one of
the provinces of the Eastern Empire
between the 6th and 9th centuries.

10

Showcase 4. Embroideries, Tapestry.

The *Resurrection* (10), woven with silk and metal thread, is a work of great value, no doubt because it was intended as an altar-cloth. It was executed in the 15th century and it is the most precious tapestry in the museum's collections.

On either side are two mitres, one of which was embroidered in the 1400's and comes from the Sainte-Chapelle in Paris (11), and the other, which used to belong to the Sommerard Collection, dates from the end of the 15th century, but nothing is known of its history.

Showcase 5. Spanish and Hispano-Mauresque Textiles.

The Moslems were responsible for the introduction of silk weaving into Spain. Some Hispano-Mauresque cloths are very similar to those of Arab workmanship from Sicily, while others are clearly different.

Woven in countries under Arab domination or that had remained Christian all the while being considerably influenced by Islamic art, these fabrics are characterized by their great richness and sumptuousness. One fragment displayed here comes from the tomb of a 13th-century Christian prince who was a friend of the Emir of Granada. Also worth mentioning are two brightly-colored embroideries that were probably executed in Moslem territory in the late Middle Ages. The magnificent band of purplish-colored silk decorated with Arabic writing is another good example of the production of the workshops established in Spain, the main centers of activity being at Seville and Granada.

10. The Resurrection
11. Embroidered mitre

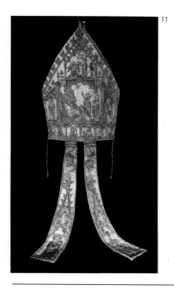

11

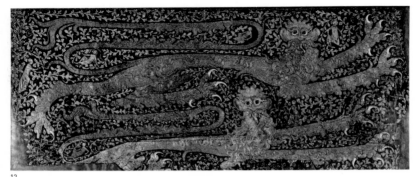

12

Above, gold embroidery on red velvet, possibly a horsecloth originally, re-adjusted in the 18th century as a chasuble presenting the leopards of England: early 14th century, most likely English (12).

Showcase 6. Mitre.

Drawn with black outlines on white silk, this mitre from the last third of the 14th century recalls the Narbonne Altarcloth in the collections of the Louvre; it probably comes from the Sainte-Chapelle in Paris (13).

Lastly, on the wall closest to the next room, there is a delicate and remarkably well-preserved piece of 13th-century Burgundian embroidery sewn with gold thread.

12. Embroidery with leopards
13. Mitre

13

Room IV

A medieval interior

Thanks to the space afforded by this particular room, we have been able to reconstitute the interior of a typical Medieval manor. The fireplace was moved from a house in Le Mans for installation here, and it dates from the end of the 15th century, as can be seen by the costumes of the figures carved on the mantel. The furniture consists of two chests, an octogonal table that can easily be taken apart and moved (1), and a sideboard (in which the lords of the manor usually displayed their gold and silver plate, the number of tiers being an indication of their rank). There is also a large chest with rounded cover wich still has its leather covering and metal fittings; it is a rare example of a type of chest that was used for transport and that is well-documented in texts. Italian furniture was already more elaborate, as can be seen by this small, late-15th century chest decorated with wood and bone marquetry featuring, on the cover and in front, three vases, and on the sides, geometric motifs of the *a certosina* type; notice also the X-chair of the same period and done in the same technique.

The Tapestries

The tapestry series known as *La vie seigneuriale* (lit. the lordly life) was purchased in 1852 from an aristocratic family of Rouen and consists of six hangings, entitled; *Embroidery* (2), *Reading*, *The Promenade*, *The Departure for the Hunt* (5), *The Bath* (3), and *Scenes of Courting*. As the general title, given in the 19th century, and the subject of each of the tapestries suggest, this series involves the evocation of the life of a lord and his lady around the year 1500.

1. Table
*2. La Vie Seigneuriale:
Embroidery*

2

Like *The Concert* in Room I, these tapestries woven with wool thread were done in the mille-fleurs style. The background, which is dark-blue for the most part, is strewn with flowering plants, in the midst of which are a few trees, and animals of all kinds. The figures float in this luxuriant vegeta- tion, placed next to one another with- out any real connection between them: they never look at each other and their feet do not touch the ground, which is non-existent anyway. This peculiar appearance can be explained by the recourse to certain labor-saving techni- ques: the weaver would re-use the de- signs for his motifs, modifying them

slightly as needed. An example of this may be seen in the figure of a lady-in-waiting which appears first in the *Bath* (3) and then again in the *Promenade* (4); the figures are identical save for a few details, in particular the colors and the head dress, which the weaver took care to vary in order to avoid monotony. For his inspiration, he could draw on the leading artists of his time: the halberdier in the *Departure for the Hunt* (5) is based on an engraving by Dürer called the Six Warriors, and dated 1495-1496. This same engraving also served as a model for *The Miracle of Saint Julian* in the Louvre and for a tapestry with a rose-colored background today in the Art Institute of Chicago. This diversity of inspiration is matched here by that of the styles: note the marvelous nude figure of the young woman in the *Bath*, standing in a basin which already features Renaissance-style acanthus leaves, while the angular folds of the drapery falling to the ground are characteristic of late 15th-century Southern Netherlandish art.

5

La Vie Seigneuriale:

3. The Bath
4. The Promenade (detail)
5. Leaving for the Hunt

Room V

Woodwork. Carpentry

Medieval craftsmen were particularly skilled in working wood and were able to exploit all of its qualities in their carpentry and cabinet-making.

The carpenters expertly cut, shaped, assembled and raised timber, using combinations of horizontal trusses and vertical king-posts, which were often decorated at the bottom and at the top: on display here are a base and two capitals, precious vestiges of an architectural decor that was often hidden from view. Timberwork that was apparent could be carved with molding, such as the two truss-bearing raf-

ters displayed on the South wall which come from the Cluny house itself. Supporting corbels were often given the most varied shapes.

"Heavy axe" carpenters did other kinds of woodwork: witness these two late 15th-century arcature fragments (South wall). The carved inscription "*Si qua fata sinant*" (if fate permits) comes from the Cathedral of Lausanne:

1. *The Resurrection of Christ*
2. *The Annunciation*

1

2

3

The 15th-century English alabaster carvings here attest to the great activity of the Nottingham workshops, which produced works on a near-industrial scale, flooding the Continent with their products (1-2). For the most part, only a few isolated panels have survived; originally painted and gilded, they were assembled into altarpieces of impressive size. They have been displayed by subject, so as to accentuate the iconographic similarities and differences. The St. Ursula placed above the door holds the attribute of her martyrdom—an arrow—and shelters her legendary 11,000 companions under her large cloak.

A 15th-century window with internal shutters has been set up in an opening that is today blocked up. Displayed in a niche is the figure of a female saint from an *Entombment*; this stone statue never has been complete, for it was placed on a stand behind the sarcophagi into which the body of Christ is being put.

3. The School
4. Mary-Magdalen Holding the Body of Christ

4

1

Room VI

The Musée de Cluny owns a very fine collection of 12th and 13th-century stained-glass which has been grouped in this room.

The oldest panels are exhibited on the North wall. The one representing *Two Monks Witnessing the Ascension of St. Benedict* was part of the stained-glass window decoration commissioned by Suger for Saint-Denis and installed for its consecration on June 11, 1144 (1).

Above, the figure *St. Timothy* comes from the church of Neuwiller-lès-Saverne (Bas-Rhin) and can be dated around 1145/50. There are also three fine fragments from the Cathedral of Troyes; the first two illustrate episodes of the legend of St. Nicholas: above, *The Jew and the Statue of St. Nicholas*, and below, the better-known episode of *The Charity of St. Nicholas* (2). The third scene comes from a series devoted to the Life of Christ; it represents *Christ Being Consoled by Angels after the Tempta-*

tion in the Desert. These three fragments were part of a series of windows which is today dispersed among several museums, and their style, which is close to certain illuminations, belongs to the Early Gothic period. These stained-glass panels may have been in the first Cathedral of Troyes, which was destroyed by a fire in 1187.

The other panels displayed on this wall were in the Church of Varennes-Jarcy in the 19th century. They include the upper part of a *Tree of Jesse*, the *Pact of Theophilus with the Devil*, a series of panels illustrating the legend of St. Martin (*The Miracle of the Fallen Tree, The Charity of St. Martin, The Apparition of Christ to St. Martin*), and the fragments of a series devoted to the Life of Christ (*The Annunciation to the Shepherds, Musician Angels*). They are in the style of stained-glass executed in the Paris region around 1220/30.

Displayed on the South and West walls are panels from the Sainte-Chapelle; they were deposited at the Musée de Cluny during the great restoration program undertaken between 1848 and 1855 and directed by F. de Guilhermy. Of the thirty panels that

1. Stained glass from Saint-Denis
2. Stained glass from Troyes

came to the museum, almost half were part of the original windows installed for the consecration in 1248; they were removed either because of their poor condition, or because their place could no longer be found. Most of these elements are exhibited on the West wall and they feature in particular: five scenes from the story of Samson (originally in bay K: Judges) (3) and a very fine medallion which probably represents *Daniel before Nebuchadnezzar* (bay G: John-the-Baptist/Daniel). The identification of the other scenes, and so the determination of their original placement in the Sainte-Chapelle, is more difficult (4).

On the South wall, above the doorway, are displayed two heraldic panels with fleur-de-lys and castille motifs, also part of the original windows, but largely reworked. On the same wall are a few panels from the original windows

3

that present considerable interpolations, like the medallion representing the *Christ and a Holy Woman*, in which the face of Christ is of late 12th-century or early 13th-century execution. The other panels exhibited on the South wall belong to restorations previous to the 19th century. Some of them are "filler" pieces that came from other buildings, like the handsome medallion depicting the *Resurrection of the Dead* (5), whose style permits a dating around 1200, and the three scenes from the story of John-the-Baptist (*The Baptism of Christ, The Dance of Salome, Salome Bringing the Head of John-the-Baptist to Herodias*), which are works from the 2nd half of the 13th century.

Some of the other panels were executed in the 15th century, probably to replace damaged windows, often reusing glass panels made in the 13th century; *Davis Playing the Harp for Saul* (bay B: Kings), *The Loss of Job's Herds* (bay D: Judith/Job) (6), *The Servant Entering the Room of Tobias and Sarah* (bay E: Jeremiah/Tobit), *Joseph Being Sold by His Brothers* (bay O: Genesis).

4

5

3. *Samson and the Lion*
4. *Adoration*
5. *The Resurrection of the Dead*
6. *The Loss of Job's Herds*

6

The East wall is illuminated by four large windows that were originally in the chapel of the royal castle at Rouen (7, 8); they were executed around 1260/70 and demonstrate the evolution of stained-glass during the 2nd half of the 13th century and in the 14th century: the colored glass is confined to the center which is surrounded by panels treated in grisaille. Represented here are figures of four apostles: St. John, St. James Major, St. Peter, and St. Paul.

Stained glass from Rouen

7. St. James and St. John
8. St. Paul

Room VII

With the creation of the museum had to be solved the delicate problem of joining the Medieval hôtel and the Roman baths. Because of the difference in level between the two buildings, a wall had to be built and a stairway installed; on this 19th-century wall have been placed a certain number of funerary slabs. Starting in the 13th century, it became the custom to carve the slabs with figures identified by inscriptions. The incised lines were usually filled in with lead, which was generally replaced in the 19th century by red paint. With the 14th century came the practice of using carved marble inlays for the face and hands on the slab. This development was accompanied by the increasing use of decoration, until finally the entire surface of the slab was covered.

The portal installed on this same wall originally belonged in the chapel of the Virgin built inside the Abbey of Saint-Germain-des-Prés under the abbotship of Hugues d'Issy (Mid-13th century). This abbot called upon the services of the great architect Pierre de Montreuil, but his spectacular constructions there

have since been lost, with the exception of this portal. According to a practice common in the Paris region, the colonnettes of the jambs alternate deep fluting with a delicate foliage decoration. Originally, the trumeau featured a statue of the Virgin and Child, but we have no idea of the original aspect of the tympanum.

On the South wall, two column-statues. The one on the right represents King David (1); its origin is unknown, but its style recalls that of the Royal Portal of Chartres (third quarter of the 12th century). The one on the left is from Paris (2); the "metallic" treatment of the folds is close to the sculptures from Senlis.

1. Column-statue: David
2. Column-statue: Prophet

Room VIII

Displayed in this room are some of he finest sculpted fragments from the Cathedral of Notre-Dame de Paris. The museum's collection contains more than 300 fragments discovered and acquired under various circumstances. It presents a complete panorama of the cathedral's exterior sculptural program executed over the hundred-year period between the mid-12th and mid-13th centuries. In 1839, excavations in the area of the Gobelins uncovered a number of statues which were immediately deposited in the *Frigidarium*. In 1845, the architect Lassus donated the head of the St. Paul from the Central Portal. Viollet-le-Duc, while he was restoring this part, in the middle of the century, deposited elements from two lintels, the figure of St. Marcel from the Central Portal, and the group of the Three Wise Men. In 1887, the museum acquired from Saint-Denis the statue of Adam. And lastly, in 1980, the Banque Française du Commerce Extérieur donated the 300 fragments discovered in the spring of 1977 under the rue de la Chaussée-d'Antin.

The Cathedral of Paris

In 1160, the bishop Maurice de Sully undertook the reconstruction of the old cathedral; work began with the choir and continued at a fairly regular pace until the erection of the façade around 1210. In the middle of the 13th century, it was decided to prolong the arms of the transept and to provide each of them with a portal. With the three portals of the façade, Notre-Dame has five portals in all. Above the portals of the façade runs the gallery of the 28 kings of Judah, the legendary ancestors of Christ. Inside, there was a vast sculptural ensemble which closed off the choir of the canons, of which only the north and south walls remain, the rood-screen (jubé) which joined them having been torn down in the 17th century; its decoration continued into the south transept, which is where the statue of Adam once stood.

The Portal of St. Anne (c. 1150)

The portal of St. Anne had originally been designed for the old cathedral, from which it was removed at the beginning of the 13th century to be erected on the new Gothic edifice, around 1210, at the same time as its upper section was completed. It can therefore be dated at around 1150, that is, not long after the three portals of Saint-Denis, completed around 1140, and shortly before the Royal Portal of Chartres (begun in 1155). The trumeau featured the statue of *St. Marcel*, Bishop of Paris, with on either side the figures of *Saints Peter and Paul* (1). The six other figures were drawn from the

1. *The Resurrection of the Dead*
2. *St. Paul*
3. *Torso*

44

Old Testament, but only that of *King David* is identifiable, thanks to the musical instrument which he held originally. As for the others, they could represent, on the left, *Solomon*, the *widow of Sarepta*, *Elijah*; and on the right, the *Sybil* and *Isaiah*.

The elongated aspect of these sculptures is explained by the fact that the column and the statue were conceived as a single load-bearing unit and carved from the same block of stone. The details of the many closely-grouped folds were sculpted with a rigor that recalls the art of the metalsmiths. The head of *David*, today in the Metropolitan Museum of Art in New York, is a characteristic example of this visionary style, whose effect must have been heightened originally when the eye was coated with lead.

The Central Portal (1210-1220)

The tympanum decoration was devoted to the Last Judgment, with scenes of the *Separation of the Good and the Evil* and of the *Resurrection of the Dead* (2), while the jambs featured the Twelve Apostles, and the trumeau the figure of Christ Blessing. The head of *St. Paul* and the three statue fragments display the monumental vision of the beginning of the century, with the bodies disappearing under close-fitting drapery with deeply carved folds. The torso even seems to have been directly inspired by Antique statuary. The head of *St. Paul*, although worn and damaged, still displays some of its original suggestive power: a characteristic detail of this is the treatment of the hair with long locks.

The lower lintel obliges us to recognize the existence of two different styles and even of two distinct periods; the angel on the left belongs to the style of the 1210's by the treatment of the drapery, while the fragment, also on the left, which introduces a new mannerist conception, must belong to the 40's.

The Portal of the Coronation of the Virgin (1210)

This portal devoted to the Virgin features her coronation on the tympanum, the saints of the diocese on the jambs, and on the trumeau a statue of the Virgin and Child. Two of the heads from this portal, an angel (4) and a prelate, display a remarkable elegance and well-delineated features. The treatment of the eye as an elongated almond shape and of the hair, which is curled in one case and well-combed in the other, indicate that they are the work of a single artist.

The Gallery of the Kings

Above the three portals, the architect installed a monumental gallery intended to house statues of the twenty-eight *kings of Judah*, the ancestors of the Christ according to the lineage set down by St. Matthew. Twenty-one of these were rediscovered in 1977 (5-6-7), bringing important evidence of the practice of polychromy in the 13th century, even if the traces of painting were rather faded. The stone was prepared with a white ground before the application of pigments mixed with a medium; the colors were laid on in flat applications, the flesh-tones being built up with glazes. To add intensity to the eyes, the pupil was rendered by a disk.

With the exception of *David* (20), none of the heads have been identified, but it may be noted that they belong more to the art of the beginning of the century than to the manneristic style of the later decades. They are the work of several sculptors and reflect very different approaches: one made very rounded heads, another preferred more elongated faces, while a third settled for conventional features. Yet another succeeded in conferring to his head a very noble bearing.

4

5

4. Head of an angel
5. David
6. King of Judah

6

The North Transept

Facing the cloister of the canons, the portal of the north transept was consecrated to the Virgin, whose statue on the trumeau escaped the depredations of the Revolution. At the jambs and their return were twelve statues: on the left, the *Three Wise Men*, on the right, the *Theological Virtues*; the rest were unidentified. The head of a king (8) and the head of a young woman (9) display the elegant and mannered style, with almond-shaped eyes prolonged by crow's-feet. Two of the fragments come from the gift-bearing kings of the Nativity, while the other two are unidentifiable. The style of this portal marks a break with the monumental style of the beginning of the century.

The figures of *Three Wise Men* which formerly decorated the eastern buttress, to the left of the portal, were carved out of the same block of stone, a remarkable accomplishment.

9

8

7. *King of Judah*
8. *Head of a king*
9. *Head of a young woman*

10

The South Transept (after 1258)

The portal facing the episcopal palace was consecrated to St. Stephen, whose statue decorated the trumeau, while the tympanum illustrated his legend. He was surrounded by figures of saints and apostles. Among these eleven torsos may be recognized that of St. Stephen, three of the apostles, a saint carrying his head (10), and two other saints, both unidentified. The style of these figures presents a considerable evolution as compared to those sculpted on the north transept: the drapery adheres closely to the body, giving a sensation of movement; some of them display a simplification which anticipates the work of the sculptors of the end of the century. One of the torsos, judging by the fall of the drapery under the elbow, is closer to the sculpture of the 14th century.

Adam (after 1258)

This remarkable nude is one of the major works of the 1260's by the undulating movement of the body and the amazingly expressive face, whose melancholy aspect is tempered by a barely perceptible smile. Originally, it was entirely painted; the skin a natural pink and the foliage of different colors (11).

10. *Decapitated saint*
11. *Adam*

11

Room IX

This spacious room has preserved to a certain extent its original proportions and aspect: the floor has been considerably raised, a modern vault replaces the one torn down in 1737, and the large arch on the South side which used to open onto the next room has been walled in, but the other walls are original: the West wall has been modified somewhat over the centuries, while the remaining two still have their old niches and windows, which recent restorations have set off to best advantage.

Exhibited in this room are some major pieces of Romanesque sculpture, including the twelve capitals from the nave of Saint-Germain-des-Prés (1-2-3) and four from the nave of Sainte-Geneviève in Paris (4-5). The former, deposited during the 19th century when the abbey church was being restored, are among the oldest examples of the sculpture of this period, that is, around the first half of the 11th century, when the nave was joined to the older porch-belfry built by the abbot Morard. This porch features a Christ in Glory (2), sculpted with a new feeling for relief, which is also to be seen on three capitals whose iconography has not yet received a satisfactory explanation. The other sculptors remained attached to more traditional formulas of relief which stands out very little from the body of the capital.

1.2.3. Capital
from Saint-Germain-des-Prés

The four frieze-capitals were placed, in the first third of the 12th century, above the columns of the first bays of the nave of Sainte-Geneviève, which was demolished in the 19th century. On two of them may be seen signs of the Zodiac, some of which do not follow the usual astrological order.

1st capital: January, with a Goat in the place of the Capricorn; March, with the Fish; May, the Bull; April, the Ram; June, the Twins (4).

2nd capital: July, the Crab; August, the Lion, and October, the Scales, which has been lost; September, the Virgin (mutilated); December, Sagittarius; November, the Scorpion; February, Aquarius, the Water-bearer.

In the middle, an early 12th-century marble wash-basin, from a cloister, where it was used by the monks for their ablutions before meals.

The fine sculpted head of a queen comes from the central portal of Saint-Denis (before 1120), an exceptional fragment of this ensemble which was mutilated three times (6).

4.5 Capital
from Sainte-Geneviève
6. Head of a queen
from Saint-Denis

Room X

Sculpture

This room is devoted to works from the Romanesque and early Gothic periods. In the middle stands an unusually small marble altar from the church of Montréjeau, in the Pyrenees. Around it are displayed a number of Romanesque capitals; the six on the left are from Catalonia (1).

Displayed on the right is a superb Burgundian pilaster from the abbey church of Cluny, around which are three capitals: the one decorated with acanthus leaves is close to Corinthian models; the other two, which are doubled and decorated with finely-carved monsters, originally surmounted paired columns in the cloister of Saint-Denis.

In the shallow, curved recess in the middle of the South wall are presented the most famous statues in the museum: four of the twelve apostles sculpted in an important workshop before 1248 for the Sainte-Chapelle, built by Saint Louis in his palace to house the relics of the Passion which he acquired from the emperor of Constantinople. They were mutilated and decapitated in 1830, but, thanks to old drawings, we have been able to match up the bodies and the heads exactly, and thus reconstitute their original appearance; one of the heads, however, is still missing. These statues were executed in a noble style which places them among the major works of sculpture of the period (2 to 6).

2

1

3

1. *Catalan capital*
2. *Apostle from the Sainte-Chapelle*
3. *St. John from the Sainte-Chapelle*
4. *Apostle from the Sainte-Chapelle*

4

5

6

Apostle from the Sainte-Chapelle.

5. *Complete*
6. *Detail*

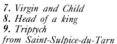

7. *Virgin and Child*
8. *Head of a king*
9. *Triptych*
from Saint-Sulpice-du-Tarn

This group is flanked by two colonnettes sculpted with a marvelous spiral pattern from the west façade of Saint-Denis; the middle part of the left one has been restored.

On the left, above the altarpiece illustrating the legend of St. Benedict, originally in the basilica of Saint-Denis (middle of the 13th century), are two fragments of the tympanum of the lower chapel of the Sainte-Chapelle (before 1248).

On the right, beneath the corbels and keystones from the chapel of the Cluny College in Paris (last third of the 13th century), there is a showcase which contains some "miniaturized" stone and ivory figures that are clearly related to monumental sculpture.

The two fine ivory statuettes of the *Virgin and Child*, one of large size,

9

standing, and the other smaller and seated (7), with drapery formed of a succession of imbricated, angular folds, are very close to Parisian monumental sculpture of the years 1250-1260. Another work of the middle of the 13th century, the small head of a king sculpted in the limestone of the Paris region, is a recent acquisition (8). Other works introduce the art of the 14th century. The Triptych of Saint-Sulpice-du-Tarn (9), remarkable for the quality of the carving, which ranges from bas-relief to work in the round, heralds the numerous diptychs and triptychs decorated with scenes of the Life of the Virgin or of Christ produced by Parisian ivory-carvers in response to the growing demand from a new clientele of private individuals.

10

The entire length of the West wall is occupied by an altarpiece which used to be in the chapel of the Virgin in the church of Saint-Germer-de-Fly (Oise); it displays all of the characteristics of Parisian art of the middle of the 13th century. Above is the tympanum of the Coronation of the Virgin from Argenteuil (third quarter of the 14th century).

Against the North wall are three statues of apostles and one of Christ from the church of Saint-Jacques-l'Hôpital in Paris; the finest one, which represents St. James (10), the patron saint of the pilgrims who flocked to this sanctuary, is displayed on the next wall; these statues were executed around 1320-1325 by Robert de Lannoy and Guillaume de Nourriche. In a space between them, on the left, is an altarpiece of the Passion, noteworthy for its openwork arcatures and pink and gold colors. Above are a few fragments of mural painting from the refectory of Charlieu (Loire); the middle scene shows King Boson of Burgundy presenting the

10. *St. James from*
Saint-Jacques-de-l'Hôpital
(detail)
11. *Fragment*
of a mural
from Charlieu

abbey of Charlieu to its founder, St. Stephen (11). On the other side, a gravestone, unfortunately incomplete, demonstrates the skill of the early tombstone carvers. Below this, a fine altarpiece from Plailly (Oise) which has retained its grandeur in spite of the mutilations that it has suffered.

On the East wall is an even more interesting engraved tombstone: it is the gravestone of a child and it does not bear a figure of the deceased, as was usually the case, but a representation of the Virgin carrying the Christ Child in a swayed pose characteristic of this period. Also on this side of the room are some corner capitals with foliated scrolls and animal motifs, and, above the doorway, an arched marble plaque bearing the magnificently-worded inscription of an archbishop of Tyre. Lastly, a wooden *Calvary* has been reconstituted on the far end of the East wall: the highly expressive figures of the Virgin and St. John are 13th-century Italian works; the Christ is a little older (12th century) and of French-perhaps Burgundian-execution; few examples of this type have been preserved in our churches.

Room XI

The sculpture of the Late Middle Ages was characterized by a return to a monumental conception, a trend which took on a particular emphasis in Burgundy. Sculptors much-impressed by the work of Claus Sluter began to wrap their own robust figures in ample drapery that dissimulated the complex forms and movements of the body, as in the Virgin of Sainte-Apollinaire (near Dijon) (1).

At the bottom of the staircase leading to Room XII may be seen a 13th-14th-century Byzantine capital featuring three warrior-saints; a very rare relief in which a *Crucifixion* is opposed to the *Suicide of Judas*, of Near Easternn workmanship, probably c. 500; the funerary inscription of the clergyman Agnomarus, dated 779, and that of Rotrude (8th-9th century); the funerary inscription of Louis VI, the son of Philip I; a few corbels and capitals sculpted in the 11th century for the church of Deuil (Val-d'Oise); and, in two recesses, the tombs from St. John of Rhodes of the five Grand-Masters of the Order of the Knights of St. John (today, the Order of Malta): the one on the right contains the ancient sarcophagus, re-used in the 14th century, of Robert de Julhiac (†1376) and that of Jean-Baptiste des Ursins (†1476), as well as the tombstone of Dieudonné de Gozon (†1353); in the one on the left are the tombs, with *gisants* (recumbent figures), of Pierre de Corneillan (†1355) and Jac-

ques de Milly (†1461), whose epitaph bears an inscription indicating that the young Prince of Antioch, Jean de Savoie (†1464) was buried "on the breast of the Grand-Master".

1. Virgin and Child
from Sainte-Apollinaire

Room XII

The small, circular room adjacent to the *Frigidarium* of the Baths presents a group of eight capitals, most of which come from Saint-Denis; they were probably executed in workshops in the Pyrenees sometime between the 5th and 7th centuries before being transported northwards (1). On the West wall are a large Corinthian capital, also in marble, found on the site of the parvis of Notre-Dame (5th-6th century), and an older composite capital (2nd century?), which used to be in Saint-Pierre de Montmartre.

Despite the ravages of the centuries, which have destroyed the rich covering materials and part of the masonry of the walls, the large *frigidarium*, or cold room, of the *Thermae* is one of the most impressive vestiges in France of the Roman occupation.

Its vast proportions—20 meters by 11 meters, with vaulting almost 14 meters

1. *Capital*
2. *The Hare Hunt*

high)—gives an idea of the grand scale on which the Romans constructed their public buildings, even in modest provincial towns like Lutetia. The walls, which feature niches, windows, and arcades, were built of small, very regular, cubical stones alternating with courses of brickwork, which served, among other things, to bind the covering material under which it was hidden; this way of building indicates, at least for Gaul, a dating around the end of the 2nd century or the beginning of the 3rd century A.D.

As for the vault—a central groin vault prolonged on three sides by barrel vaults—, it is the largest one of its kind remaining from the Gallo-Roman period; the hanging gardens set on top of it during the Middle Ages in no way weakened its structure. Recent restorations have consolidated the facing material, large patches of which can still be seen on the intrados.

A room so unique and so majestic deserved to be presented for its own sake, free of the clutter of objects and exhibits. The middle has therefore been left empty, to set off the loftiness of the space, and along the walls only a few appropriate pieces of antique sculpture have been put on display: on the North side, a bull found in the masonry of the bell tower of the old church of Saint-Marcel, a frieze depicting a hare hunt (2), which was probably part of a funerary monument, a relief with three torsos from a victory monument, and a fragment of a medallion floor mosaic from a Roman colony in Africa. On the South side, three col-

3

umn shafts from the old Cathedral of St. Stephen's, found under the parvis of Notre-Dame; on the same side, three more blocks carved with reliefs (2nd century), found on the site of the church of Saint-Landry, on the Ile de la Cité (3); on the best-preserved one are figures of three divinities, *Vesta* (?) holding a torch, *Vulcan*, and *Mars*, handled in a remarkably free style.

Displayed on the East side are a few more Roman or Gallo-Roman sculptures, a mosaic fragment which may have been part of the original decoration of these baths, and a Gallic inscription. The exhibit of greatest interest, however, is the series of blocks (4) in the Northwest corner of the room which used to be piled up to form a pillar like the one preserved in Mainz; the five elements here, two of which form a complete base, were found in 1711 under the Cathedral of Notre-Dame and they represent both Gallic and Roman divinities: *Mars*, *Venus*, *Fortuna*, *Mercury*, *Castor* and *Pollux*, *Cernunnos* (the god with antlers), *Smertrios*, *Jupiter*, *Vulcan*, *Esus*, *Tarvos trigaranus* (the bull with three cranes); the last block is carved with six armed fi-

gures which probably represent the "Nautes du Parisis", the Paris boatmen who erected this pillar dedicated to Jupiter under the reign of Tiberius (14-37 A.D.), as the inscription indicates: TIB(ERIO) CAESARE AUG-(USTO) IOVI OPTUMO MAXSUMO S(SAC-RUM) NAUTAE PARISIACI PUBLICE POSIERUNT.

The Baths themselves were probably built by this same corporation of *nautes*, which apparently had the monopoly of river traffic on the Seine; in support of this hypothesis are two corbels at the spring of the great vault which are decorated with ships' prows laden with arms.

An alcove below floor-level on the West side of the room contains several stone sarcophagi found in the 19th century during excavations of old Parisian sanctuaries; they date from the 6th-8th centuries.

3. Blocks from Saint-Landry
4. "Pillar of the Nautes"

4

Staircase
(from Room XI to Room XIII)

1. *Lérian and Laureolle*
2. *A Battle
and an Embarkation*

Displayed on the wall of the staircase leading to the first floor are a number of epitaphs: of particular interest is the one in memory of the famous Parisian alchemist Nicolas Flamel. Two tapestries illustrate episodes from literature in vogue during the late Middle Ages: the story of Lérian and Lauréolle (1), and *a Battle and an Embarkation* (2). The painted altarpiece bearing the arms of Aragon is dedicated to St. Martin.

Room XIII

The Lady with the Unicorn

The six tapestries of the *Dame à la licorne* series is undoubtedly one of the finest works of art that has come down to us from the late Middle Ages. In the nearly one hundred years that it has been in the Musée de Cluny's collections, its fame has attracted visitors from all over the world. So enthralling is its charm and poetry that it is easy to believe the many picturesque legends which it has inspired.

Its more recent history has done nothing to dispel the aura of mystery with which some have surrounded it. Its popularity was due initially to the famous author George Sand who, in 1844, was the first to draw public attention to these tapestries, which at the time were hung in the apartment of a local official in the Château de Boussac. Not long before, another writer, Prosper Mérimée, then inspector for the Monuments Historiques, had reported on their deplorable condition and recommented their acquisition, but to no avail. It was only in 1882 that negotiations for their acquision by the Musée de Cluny were successfully concluded. In the meantime these tapestries had captured the imagination of even the most serious scholars, and legends began to abound. Because of the profusion of crescents, some fancied an Oriental inspiration, while the presence of the young woman suggested ideas of a spurned romance. Combined together, these two elements evoked the sad fate of prince Zizim, who, after having been driven from his homeland and imprisoned at Bourganeuf, near Boussac, supposedly had it woven out of nostalgia for his lady love. The errors in this theory have since been demonstrated, but what persisted was the idea that because of the constant presence of the young woman, the series must have been related to a betrothal or a marriage.

None of these theories, however, find confirmation in the analysis of the heraldic and iconographic motifs. The coat-of-arms consisting of *gules and a band azure bearing three crescents* have long been identified as those of the Le Viste family of Lyons, a family of famous jurists which established itself at an early date in Paris, where its members distinguished themselves in Royal office and in the Parliament. Barthélémy became counsellor in 1440, to be succeeded in this function by his son Aymé, who died in 1484, leaving two sons. The eldest son, Jean, who was appointed to the highest office of the Court of Appeals, died in 1500 without leaving a male heir. His brother Aubert, who died before him in 1493, left only one son, Antoine, who was the last to bear the family arms. When the tapestry set was believed to have been a betrothal or marriage present, attempts were made to identify the lucky bride. According to heraldry, however, these arms can only be those of a man, for they are *full*; had it been otherwise, they would have been divided into two parts, with the husband's arms at dexter and those of the father of the bride's at sinister. The only member of the Le Viste family who can be retained, for reasons of datation and succession which are too complex to mention here, is Jean Le Viste. This permits us to date the execution of the tapestries between 1484, the date at which Jean took over the family arms at the death of his father, and 1500, the date of his own death.

The iconography of the tapestries, another topic of much debate, has now been elucidated, for it has been established that the six pieces constituted the entire set and that this was the order in which they were hung at the Château de Boussac in the 18th century. The subject of five of them are the senses, a theme not uncommon in the Middle Ages.

1. The Lady with the Unicorn
Sight

Sight: the Lady holds a mirror which reflects the head of the unicorn (1-2).
Hearing: the Lady plays a portable organ while her maidservant pumps the bellows (7).
Taste: the young woman picks a sweet from a bowl, a pet monkey below takes one to its mouth and the parakeet holds another in its claws (8).
Smell: the Lady makes a garland of carnations while the monkey sniffs one that he has filched from the basket (5-6-9).
Touch: with her left hand, the young woman delicately holds the horn of the unicorn (4).

The sixth piece (3-10), which shows the Lady standing in front of a majestic tent with open flaps, for a long time defied all interpretation. Contrary to what has generally been thought, the young woman is in fact depositing the necklace into the casket held by her maidservant. She is therefore in the act not of choosing a jewel, but of renouncing her jewelry. In the light of this reading, the inscription above the tent, "A mon seul désir" (to my sole desire), becomes self-explanatory and gives the key to the meaning of her gesture. This scene is related to the idea of *Liberum arbitrium*, considered by the philosophers of Antiquity as being the faculty which leads us to right action, unless

2

3

it is hindered by the passions, that is by our capitulation to the senses. This interpretation might seem far-fetched, were it not for the fact that it is supported by the existence of another tapestry set: in the rich collections of the Cardinal de La Mark was a series of six tapestries known as *Los Sentidos*; five of them represented the senses, and the sixth featured the inscription *Liberum arbitrium*.

The Lady with the Unicorn

2. *Sight (detail)*
3. *"A mon seul désir »*

This series offers another reading which involves the heraldic motifs. Indeed, the insistent repetition of Jean Le Viste's coat-of-arms calls for an explanation: they are represented as many as four times in *Smell* and *Taste*, and the lances with banners and pennants are weapons, because tipped with sharp points. Also, the tent in the sixth piece was more a feature of the battlefield than of domestic life. This association of arms with a profane—and peaceful—allegory, was nothing less than a way for Jean Le Viste to manifest his pretentions to nobility. In his testament, he went so far as to ask that he be represented in a stained-glass window of his chapel "as a knight dressed in armour". This man of law who was rewarded with the highest honors—including the supreme honor of being buried in the chapel of the Célestins in Paris—, like so many of his contemporaries who had come to the capital from the provinces, fervently aspired to be admitted into the spheres of nobility. He was among those whose hopes were not to be fulfilled.

4

5

6

The Lady with the Unicorn

4. *Touch*
5. *Smell (detail)*
6. *Smell*

7

8

Part of the fame of the *Lady with the Unicorn* comes from its harmonious color scheme. A limited number of hues in a variety of shades were used to render the many different elements of the composition. This restrained palette helps to create the feeling of a poetic enchantment.

The Lady with the Unicorn

7. Hearing
8. Taste

The dark-blue, rounded "islet" which serves as a ground for each of the scenes is dotted with flowering plants and set against a background varying in color from red to rose, and which is itself strewn with detached, blossoming branches. This type of decoration is documented as having been commonly used in Medieval tapestries, but few of the pieces themselves have survived. This marvellous decor highlights the elegance of the young woman, who appears in different attitudes and costumes, the splendor of which further enhances the great beauty of this work.

9

10

The Lady with the Unicorn

9. *Smell*
10. "*A mon seul désir*" (detail)

Room XIV

This room has been equipped with air-conditioning to protect the museum's large collection of painted panels and polychrome sculpture. Around these fragile works have been assembled contemporary sculptures and tapestries, to give an idea of the artistic production in Northern Europe (France, Germany, Southern Netherlands, England) during the 14th and 15th centuries.

Among the 14th-century works may be seen not a few representations of the Virgin and Child, which is not surprising, for statues of this type were produced in such great numbers that they are still plentiful today, in churches and in museums alike. More precious are the works in marble, such as the figures of the *Virgin* (1) and of *St. John* (2), which may have been in the Abbey of the Dames-des-Longchamp, and especially the *Presentation in the Temple* (3), whose quality speaks for the work of a major artist active under the reign of Charles V.

Above the entrance is a *Crucifixion*, a rare example of painting from this period, from the church of Sauvagnat (near Issoire, Puy-de-Dôme).

1. The Virgin
2. St. John

3. The Presentation in the Temple

4

In the showcases are displayed works of smaller size, although some are nonetheless monumental in character; for instance, the *Road to Calvary* (4) in gilded and polychrome wood, which

5

dates from the 1400's and was perhaps sculpted in Flanders, or the marble figure of *St. Paul* (5) of the same period. These works contrast with the altarpiece fragments depicting a *Road to Calvary* and an *Entombment* in the more precious and linear style of the early 14th century.

To the left of this showcase hang two paintings donated to the Cathedral of Amiens by the corporation of painters at the beginning of the 16th century; they represent the Consecration of David (with a fine Pietà on the back) and that of Louis XII (6), in accordance with the rites of the Royal Consecrations at the Cathedral of Rheims (note the figures presenting the ceremonial sword and spurs, preserved today in the Louvre).

4. *The Road to Calvary*
5. *St. Paul*
6. *The Consecration of Louis XII*
7. *The Averbode Altarpiece*

On the South wall, a 16th-century carved altarpiece decorated with scenes of the *Passion*; together with the *Averbode Altarpiece* on the East wall, it evokes the intense activity of the specialized workshops in Antwerp which turned out these works on an almost industrial scale. They are of good quality and their original colors are nearly intact.

Particularly rare for its subject-matter is the *Averbode Altarpiece* (7), which depicts the *Mass of St. Gregory* along with the *Meeting of Melchizedech and Abraham*, and the *Last Supper*; exceptional too is the fact that we know the name of its author and its date: Jan de Molder, 1513.

Among the examples of Flemish painting of the Late Middle Ages one stands out by its originality: it shows a scene from the *Life of St. Géry*, the patron-apostle of Brussels (8), which is the birthplace of the Master of the View of St. Gudule, to whom it is attributed.

Around it are later works: a painting by the Confraternity of Abbeville which shows the church of Saint-Wulfran, and the famous *Virgin of the Wheatstalk*, of the same provenance.

On the panel opposite them are two small pictures representing a pope and *St. Margaret*, examples of Portuguese painting, while the two musical subjects (which may have decorated a portable organ) were probably executed in the Northern Netherlands.

8. Scene from the Legend of St. Géry
9. *St. John*

11

10

German sculpture is richly represented in this room, in particular by the statuette of a female saint, possibly *St. Martha*, commissioned by a confraternity of penitents who had themselves represented with their hoods. Of similar origin are the figures of the *Virgin* and of *St. John* (9) from a *Calvary* which display a marked taste for bright and bold colors. Prominently displayed in the center of the room is a small altarpiece, a precious work both for its painted panels and its sculpture, which depicts the *Lamentation of Christ* (10, 11); it comes from the Duchy of Clèves, and the village of Bethlehem represented in the Adoration of the Magi was modelled on the Germain town of Kranenburg, at the border of the Netherlands. On the back is a *Seated Virgin* (12) which recalls the manner of Enrik Douvermann, a sculptor active in the Kalkar region in the early 16th century.

Altarpiece:

The Lamentation of Christ
10. *Complete*
11. *Detail*
12. *Seated Virgin*

12

14

Before continuing with sculpture, we would mention three altarpieces; one of them, painted in England around 1320 with scenes of the *Life of the Virgin* (13), is a priceless piece in the museum's collections, for the works of the English primitives are not only rare, but there are few in France.

In a wholly other vein is the *Pietà of Tarascon* (14), a Provençal work dating from the middle of the 15th century; it is the altarpiece of "Our Lord in the arms of Our Lady" mentioned in the 1457 inventory of the Château de Tarascon, at which date it was described as being "new" and decorating the "new room of the Queen," Jeanne de Laval, the second wife of King René.

We return to sculpture with some wooden statuettes which were painted originally, but unfortunately scraped down in the 19th century.

Prominently displayed are two of the finest Brabantian works in the museum's collections: a half-length Virgin from Louvain (15) and a Mary-Magdalen from Brussels (16) whose elegant and coquettish aspect seems to belong more to the sphere of the profane than to that of the sacred.

13

15

13. *Altarpiece of the Life of the Virgin*
(detail)
14. *The Pietà of Tarascon*
15. *Virgin and Child*

16

Two showcases present altarpiece fragments of painted wood, most of which come from the workshops of Antwerp or of the Southern Netherlands. The first one contains remnants of an altarpiece from Ourscamp (Oise), decorated with three scenes from the strange legend of the *Santa Casa of Lorette*. Dominating the second is a poignant representation of the *Virgin Fainting* (17), an example of the high quality of the Brussels workshops.

The presentation of sculpture from the Late Middle Ages ends with works in stone executed in different regions of France. From Champagne is the statue of St. Barbara (18), on the right, a replica of which is in the church of Saint-Urbain in Troyes. Another work from that region may be the charming *Mary-Magdalen* kneeling before a group of the *Coronation of the Virgin* in a more angular style, a work from Lorraine.

18

17

16. *St. Mary-Magdalen*
17. *The Virgin Fainting*
18. *St. Barbara*

19

On the North wall hangs the tapestry of the *Prodigal Son* (19-20-21), formerly part of a series, the rest of which has since been lost. The three scenes—the Farewell, the Departure, and the Return—are framed by pillars which were originally completed by arcades. The costumes and the decor already in the Renaissance style speak for a dating around the first quarter of the 16th century. The bottom section is speckled with flowers which also appear in the rolling landscape above, dotted with palaces, castles, and genre scenes.

On the East wall, the *Story of Daniel* is depicted on a large tapestry of standard production; on the right, Nebuchadnezzar making preparations to massacre the wise men of Babylon; on the left, Daniel explaining to him the dream of the silver-footed giant, who is represented at the top left.

20

21

The Prodigal Son
19. *Complete*
20.21. *Details*

Corridor XV

On the South wall of this long corridor is displayed a group of carved woodwork which includes the priests' stalls from the chapel of Picardy in the rue du Fouarre, consecrated in 1506. Opposite is a door which is one of the first examples in Paris of the Renaissance style.

Several showcases contain domestic objects: harness fittings, coin "treasures" found in hiding-places, a small book.

Seals

Seals were a way of validating an act by an individual or an association of individuals. Displayed here are matrices carved with the inverse of the design that was stamped on the hot wax. The spindle-shaped seal of Margaret of Constantinople, Countess of Flanders (1244-1280), shown standing between two lions rampant, is made of green wax, as is the magnificent seal of majesty of Philippe le Bel. As for the equestrian seal of Guillaume I of Hainault, it is made of red wax, as is that of Robert, Duke of Bar (1352-1411).

Games

In the middle of this showcase, placed on a very fine late 15th-century chest bearing the arms of the Chambellan family of Dijon, is a 15th-century game box (1), a piece which is unique as much by its quality as by its rarity. The different sliding panels feature a variety of games, including backgammon. The wood is decorated with colored bone and ivory inlays. Around it are displayed some chess pieces made of bone engraved with geometric designs, two ivory checkers, all from the 12th century, two large pawns representing seated figures (2) and a large die.

2

1. Game box
2. Chess pawn

1

88

Room XVI

In the display unit in the middle of the room, **Showcase 1** (on the left) contains three of the votive crowns, two of the crosses, several pendants, and various suspension elements from a 7th-century Visigoth treasure found at Guarrazar, near Toledo, around the middle of the 19th century (1-2-3). These are some of the very few remaining ex-votos of a type that was originally suspended above church altars: the Christianized Germanic invaders of the former territories of the Occidental Roman Empire in fact adopted a Byzantine practice whose existence is known to date back to the 5th-6th centuries, as evidenced by texts as well as by illuminations. The stones—for the most part, sapphires, emeralds, rock crystal, and mother-of-pearl—were mounted, their irregular shapes being preserved, as was the practice in the High Middle Ages; certains parts were done in cloisonné, such as the R-shaped pendant, the only element of the crown of King Recceswinthe remaining in the museum's collections (the crown and other pieces from the same ensemble, today in Madrid, were the object of an "exchange" between the French and Spanish governments during the Second World War).

1.2.3. Votive crown from Guarrazar

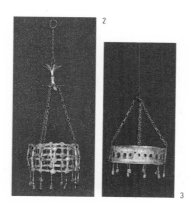

In the middle of **Showcase 2** is displayed the *Golden Rose* of Basel (4-5). There was an ancient tradition according to which the pope would commission a golden rose for the rituals of the fourth Sunday of Lent *(Laetare)*, which would then be given as a token of thanks or to honor a particular person or city. Recent research has identified this *Golden Rose* as being the one executed in 1330 by the goldsmith Minucchio da Siena for the Avignon Pope John XXII, who presented it to one of the counts of Neuchâtel, probably Rudolph, Lord of Nidau and Count of Neuchâtel, whose coat-of-arms is stamped on the base.

This *Golden Rose* is the oldest one known; the others that have come down to us are dated no earlier than the second half of the 15th century.

Showcase 3 contains jewelry and coins from the Gallic period. The civilization of the Gauls, of which relatively few traces remain, was amazingly active in this area of production. A very rich collection of jewels, discovered more often than not by chance, has been assembled and distributed between the Musée de Cluny, the Bibliothèque Nationale, and the Musée des Antiquités Nationales at Saint-Germain-en-Laye.

The chain with six uneven links was founded in 1844 in a tomb in the forest on Carnoët (Finistère) along with other objects of lesser value which are preserved at Saint-Germain-en-Laye. The spiral bracelet comes from a sarcophagus found in the valley of the Ariège. In 1856, at Saint-Marc-le-Blanc (Ille-et-Vilaine), near Rennes, was unearthed an important treasure which had probably been hidden by a Gallic goldsmith during a period of strife; it included raw ingots and barely-worked jewels which have not been preserved. The Musée de Cluny acquired only the finished pieces: two rings and seven bracelets.

The Golden Rose

4. Complete
5. Detail

4

5

7

Showcase 5 presents more objects from the High middle Ages and others from the Roman period. Among the former are two "peacock tail" fibulae (1st century A.D.) and eight fibulae with champlevé enamel decoration (2nd-3rd centuries) (8). The second group also includes fibulae, most of then of Frankish origin: pieces featuring a large bird-shaped pin with garnets in cloisonné (late 5th-6th century), some with a head in a half-moon and finger shapes (6th-early 7th centuries), and others that are symmetrical (7th-9th centuries); there are also a necklace and pendants with glass beads, and other items of feminine adornment of the 6th-7th centuries. The bronze buckle-plates were used, according to their size, either on belts or on leather shoe straps; they also come from Frankish tombs of the northern regions of Gaul (6th-7th centuries), except for the largest one, which belongs to a more or less contemporary type from Aquitaine. Lastly, notice the pieces of

6. *Torques*
7. *Reliquary casket*
8. *Enamelled fibula*

The spiral torques with double hooks at the ends came from a sealed earthen pot found in 1854 in the township of Cesson (Ille-et-Vilaine). The two most beautiful pieces in this showcase—the torques: one made of four striated strands twisted together (6), and the other of a large braid with a hook at the end—were discovered in 1886 at Montgobert (Aisne), on uncultivated land owned by Louis de Cambacérès, who donated them to the museum.

Showcase 4 (to the left of the entrance) contains pieces from the High Middle Ages. Next to Merovingian rings, a pin with a garnet cabochon, and polyhedral pendants typical of contemporary feminine dress (5th-6th centuries), are displayed a "Lombard" pectoral cross with stamped ornamentation, a scabbard with a gilt sword-guard from Villeneuve-la-Garenne, a Carolingian swordbelt "clasp" with filigree decoration, and a silver-gilt casket-reliquary representing the *Virgin between St. Peter and St. Paul* of a type that was apparently very common throughout the West during the 7th and 8th centuries (7).

6

8

Visigoth funerary furnishings found in Southwest Gaul: a belt plaque with cloisonné glasswork, a pair of eagle-shaped fibulae also done in cloisonné (9), and a gilt bronze buckle-plaque (6th century).

Showcase 6 contains Late Roman and Byzantine cloisonné enamelwork and glyptics. Notice, first of all, the two rock-crystal lion heads (10), probably the ornaments of a ceremonial chair, the only examples of their kind preserved from late antiquity. The child's head is an antique chalcedony "saphirine" to which a gold mount was added in the 14th-15th century.

The small, translucent and cloisonné enamel plaque representing full-length figures of Saints Matthew and Luke was made during the Middle Byzantine period.

Displayed in the middle of **Showcase 7** is a portable altar executed in England during the first half of the 11th century (11); the figures engraved on the silver leaf surrounding the center stone are characterized by a brisk line that makes for undulating and often animated contours, a feature typical of the style of Winchester that was to spread throughout Europe during the High Middle Ages.

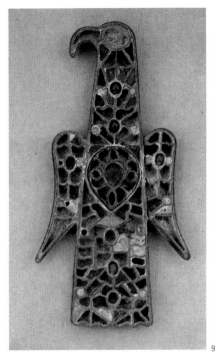

9

9. Eagle-shaped fibula
10. Lion heads
11. Portable altar
12. Binding of a Gospel

10

On the other hand, the works around it are of French origin and date from the 12th century. The large *Christ Blessing* and the statuette of a female saint are similar in many respects to the sculptures of the Romanesque portals. The two croziers are examples of two different types common in the 12th century; the volute of the first, decorated with a single leaf, is of a simpler design; the other, which comes from the Abbey of Clairvaux, features the Paschal Lamb; it must be a later work and may be situated around the end of the 12th or beginning on the 13th century.

In the middle of **Showcase 8** are displayed two Italian works. The origin of the silver-gilt Gospel binding has been identified as Novara, for the first two bishops of this town are represented among the portraits of the saints that form a frame around the depiction of the *Traditio Legis* (Christ giving the keys to St. Peter and the book to St. Paul) (12). This book cover demonstrates various techniques of the Medieval goldsmiths, and in particular the use of a mixture of earth and wax to "support" the silver figures in shallow relief, and the use in the inscriptions and foliated scrolls of niello, a sulphur and silver compound which gives a dark-grey color.

The gilt-brass cross with engraved decoration belongs to a small group of crosses that is sometimes said to be of Germanic origin, but which was probably executed in Italy during the first half of the 12th century. Also worthy of

11

12

mention in this showcase are two objects—a ring and a medallion—found buried at Gometz-le-Châtel (Essonne), along with some 11th-century coins.

In **Showcase 9** there is an engraved brass cross of Tuscan workmanship than can be dated to the 13th century. The other objects displayed in this showcase come from Northern France or the Meuse region and date from the beginning of the 13th century; a hand-warmer decorated with bust-length figures of the apostles, a hand-warmer's cup with figures of the *Seven Liberal Arts*, a stemmed pyxis, a large quadrilobe reliquary, the back of which is decorated with scrolls executed with a brown varnish made from a heated preparation of linseed oil and often used in the Mosan region during the 12th century.

Showcase 10 contains works from the Rhineland-Meuse region and from Germany. The very fine stemmed reliquary in the middle which features engraved, openwork, filigree, and nielloed decoration, comes from the collegial church of Notre-Dame de Termonde (13). The figures present supple and flowing drapery that was typical of a style widely practiced around the year 1200. Above, the openwork plaque decorated with figures representing the *Four Rivers of Paradise* was probably part of a book binding originally (14). It is undoubtedly one of the masterpieces of the Mosan goldsmiths and was executed around the middle of the 12th century. The other objects are decorated with champlevé enamels on brass. Particularly noteworthy is the semi-circular plaque of very refined workmanship representing a *Crucifixion*, executed in the region of Hildesheim (Lower Saxony) around 1160-1170 (15).

13. Reliquary
14. The Rivers of Paradise
15. Crucifixion

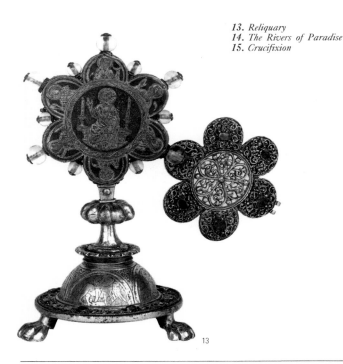

13

14

15

17

18

In Showcases 11 to 24 is presented the Musée de Cluny's superb collection of Limoges enamels.

Showcase 11 contains a few pieces that were of prime importance for the beginnings of enamel-making in Limoges. The *Christ in Majesty*, with its

16

hieratic features and superbly billowing drapery (16), formerly belonged to the Spitzer Collection and was matched with a *Crucifixion* preserved today at the Valencia de Don Juan Institute in Madrid. Certain of its technical and stylistic aspects present undeniable similarities with the enamels from the tomb of Silos (Museo Arqueólogico, Burgos), executed in Spain around 1160-1170, while others are close to the works of the West of France and herald the production in Limoges of the late 12th century; these works raise the question of the relations between Spain and the then budding Limousin enamel industry.

16. Christ in Majesty
17.18. Plaques from Grandmont

The two plaques of the *Adoration of the Magi* and of the *Conversation of Etienne de Muret with his Disciple Hugo Lacerta* (17-18) were undeniably executed in Limoges: they come from the high altar of Grandmont and were executed shortly after 1189, the date of the canonization of St. Etienne de Muret; these two plaques have justifiably been called the "incunabula" of the Limoges enamels.

The other works presented in this cabinet also belong to the early period of the activity of the Limousin workshops. The large plaque from a cross, the *symbols of the Evangelists*, and the *St. Peter*, which probably came from the Grandmont Priory of Mathons (Haute-Marne), present so many affinities with the "Grandmont Plaques" that they have been attributed to the same workshop.

In the middle of **Showcase 12** is displayed a large cross (19) which, in the 19th century, belonged to Abbey of Bonneval (Aveyron) and was acquired by the museum in 1978. Its style presents affinities with the large quadrilobe plaque from a reliquary of St. Francis of Assisi which represents the saint receiving the stigmata (20). These two pieces belong to a group of fairly heterogenous works which, for historical and inconographic reasons, are considered by some to have been executed in Italy—by artisans from Limoges who settled there or by local craftsmen taking their inspiration from Limoges enamels. Indeed, there are obvious

19. *Cross from Bonneval*
20. *Plaque from a reliquary of St. Francis of Assisi*

analogies between these and Limousin works of the late 12th and early 13th centuries, as can be seen, for example, by a comparison with a "roofless" Limoges reliquary which features vermicular patterns and bust-length figures of apostles (21). These "vermicular" backgrounds—a finely engraved and dense tendril ornamentation—are characteristic of a large group of late 12th-century and early 13th-century Limoges works which otherwise present stylistic differences, visible in the three such works displayed here.

The following showcases give an idea of the great diversity in the enamelwork produced by the craftsmen of Limoges. Diversity as to the types of objects: shrines (châsse)—from the small reliquary of St. Thomas à Becket (22) (Sh. 13), to the large reliquaries of the Life of Christ (Sh. 16) and of St. Fausta (23) (Sh. 18)—, crosses, bookbinding plates (Sh. 15), chandeliers (Sh. 16), censers (Sh. 21), a Eucharistic dove (24) (Sh. 21) and pyxides for the Host (Sh. 14), croziers (Sh. 14), free-standing figures (Sh. 20), head-reliquaries, "gemellion" bowls for ablutions (Sh. 24), cover plaques, medallions, applique figures or groups for the decoration of large pieces (Sh. 13).

21

21. Reliquary
with vermiculated decoration
22. Reliquary
of St. Thomas à Becket

22

23

24

*23. Great reliquary
of St. Fausta
24. Eucharistic
Dove*

A diversity of techniques too: although we have been unable to establish a chronological sequence, we may observe that the practice of enamelling the figures and reserving the backgrounds characteristic of the early phase of production was progressively reversed, with the figures being either reserved and engraved, or set into an enamelled ground that was decorated more often than not with rosettes and scrolls with large stylized flowers.

Similarly, the varied and bold palettes of the 11th century tended to weaken afterwards, with blues, and especially the lavender blue so characteristic of Limoges works, dominating more and more.

25

There was a diversity of styles as well; here again, it is difficult to determine an exact chronology, but it is evident that between the last decades of the 12th century and the second half of the 13th century the craftsmen of Limoges were open to different artistic currents. Thus, many works generally attributed to the late 12th century, such as the two *châsses* with vermicular patterns in Showcase 12, feature a marked Romanesque stylization. The *"1200 style"*, characterized primarily by drapery with tight, finely-traced folds and sagging curves, is to be observed more or less clearly in many works of the first half of the 13th century: for example, the large *châsse* of St. Fausta (Sh. 18), the three very finely-executed open-work medallions decorated with biblical subjects—the *Creation of Man*, the *grapes of the Promised Land* (25), *Moses Striking the Rock*—(Sh. 13), and the figure of St. Paul in light relief (Sh. 18) of equally high quality. There is, however, a group of work which features roundish faces, often with almond-shaped eyes, drapery with deep folds ending with "teardrop" or pointed beak shapes, which reflect the "stylistic revolution" that occurred in Paris around 1240: among the finest examples of these are the two applique groups representing the *Last Supper* (26) and the *Flagellation* (Sh. 20), elements of an ensemble illustrating the *Life and Pas-*

sion of Christ and dispersed among several museums; of lesser quality, and probably of later date, is the *Virgin of Moussac*, which is another, more monumental, expression of this movement.

We would also mention the great diversity in the quality of these works from Limoges: some rank among the masterpieces of this period—in particular the Spitzer Christ and the Grandmont Plaques (Sh. 11)—, while others, produced on a near-industrial scale, feature very perfunctory motifs or prefabricated elements used in an assembly-line fashion: this was the case for many of the indispensable liturgical accessories—crosses, censers and incense-boats, pyxides, etc.—destined for sale at low prices to churches of modest means.

The activity of the Limousin workshops continued during the second half of the 13th century and into the 14th, but seems to have been on a smaller scale, of lesser quality, and it is difficult to distinguish their production from that of other workshops in other regions of the West and Southwest of France. Showcase 24 contains works generally

25. *Grapes*
from the Promised Land
26. *The Last Supper*
27. *Reliquary*
from the Sainte-Chapelle

26

atributed to Limoges, datable by their style to the 2nd half of the 13th or early 14th century. Notice in particular the two enamelled ciboria, a rare type of object among the earlier remaining Limoges pieces.

Showcase 37, in the middle, presents 13th-century precious metalwork from France. The most precious piece is the small silver-gilt reliquary from the Treasury of the Sainte-Chapelle (27); it was executed in 1261 to contain the relics of Saints Lucien, Julien, and Maxien, collected at Beauvais in the presence of Saint Louis. The front features three rectangular openings to permit viewing of the relics. On the back, the figures of the three decapitated saints display amazingly precise and refined workmanship. The style of these figures and of the architecture of the reliquary recall the finest contemporary works of illumination, monumental sculpture, and architecture. Of

27

equally fine quality is the engraved decoration of the almond-shaped plaque—most likely the base of an arm-reliquary—representing the death of St. Victor, angels raising his soul to heaven, and his reception by Christ (28); this work comes from the Abbey of Montieramey (Aube) and the inscription engraved around the border indicates that it was executed in 1243 and commissioned by Abbot Philip.

This Showcase also contains cross-reliquaries of the True Cross, with double crossbars and filigree work (29). We know that a good number of relics of the Cross of Christ were sent to the West after the capture of Constantinople by Crusaders in 1204. To house these most precious of relics, reliquaries of different forms were made, but most adopted the form of the double-barred Byzantine cross; the fragment of the True Cross was placed at the main crossing, generally along

with other relics set into compartments at the ends of the cross-bars. The filigree decoration, so common in Western Europe during the first half of the 13th century, is characteristic of several large groups of this type of cross. The origin of the Musée de Cluny's two crosses is unknown, but the detail of the filigree suggests that they belong to a group executed in the Limousin region.

28. *Plaque from a reliquary of St. Victor*
29. *Filigree Cross*

29

28

Showcase 36 displays jewels from the 12th-15th centuries. The two enamelled plaquettes with attached rings were probably sewn on clothes (30-31). These are known as *émaux "de plique"*—to quote a term used in 14th-century inventories—, that is, a type of cloisonné enamel characterized by translucent enamelled motifs (clover leaves, hearts, rosettes, etc.).

Many of the jewels presented in this cabinet are part of what is known as the "Colmar Treasure," a cache of jewelry and coins found in 1853 in the wall of a house of the rue des Juifs in Colmar, probably hidden there in 1349 during the persecution of the Jews that followed the Great Plague. Most of these jewels date from the first half of the 14th century and include the principal types then in use: rings, clasps, belts, costume ornaments.

Showcase 38 contains a variety of objects, most of them of small size, dating from the 14th and 15th centuries. Displayed on the back panel is a large clasp-reliquary featuring an eagle with outspread wings and decorated with enamels and gemstones (32); it was executed around the midle of the 14th century in Bohemia or the North of Italy. Among the works decorated with translucent enamels in light relief, we would mention by the very fine mid-14th-century Sienese medallion representing *St. Galgano*, and a curious reliquary-medallion decorated on the front with gemstones and on the back with a gilt-silver plaque which represents the *Christ of the Column* in the presence of two donors executed in translucent enamels; the costumes of the latter figures permit an attribution to a French artist working during the reign of Charles V (1364-1380).

*30.31. Plaquettes
in "émail de plique"*
32. Clasp-reliquary

32

30/31

103

Showcase 25 presents chalices of the 14th and 15th centuries. Note especially a 14th-century chalice acquired in 1982 (33), identifiable as the work of a Mosan artist thanks to the inscription written in the vernacular. The three chalices with enamelled knops placed around it are Italian; one of them bears the name and coat-of-arms of the Tuscan family of Tuciarelli.

Showcase 26 contains late 13th and 14th century works of diverse origin decorated for the most part with champlevé enamels on brass. The three cross plaques representing the *Virgin*, the *Pelican*, and *St. Luke* were executed in the Upper Rhineland in the late 13th century. The splendid casket-reliquary of the *Life of the Virgin* is generally held to be a French work (34). The large clasp featuring an *Annunciation* belongs to a group of clasps whose style speaks for a French origin and a dating around the middle

33. Chalice
34. Reliquary of the Life of the Virgin

of the 14th century. On the other hand, the beautiful censer with an engraved decoration and, on the cover, the Angel the Virgin of the *Annunciation* is of Italian origin, probably Sienese, from the middle of the 14th century.

Showcase 27 features a large silver processional cross decorated with translucent enamel plaquettes representing angels (35-36). The hallmark of Barcelona (+BA/RCK) stamped on the silver leaves indicates its place of origin; it is datable to the middle or second half of the 14th century.

33

34

Cross with the hallmark of Barcelona

35. *Complete*
36. *Detail*

36

35

Very few pieces of secular precious metalwork from the Middle Ages have come down to us. In **Showcase 28** are displayed the works of this type in the Musée de Cluny's collections, including the hanaps and the goblet from the "Treasure of Gaillon"; one of the hanaps is stamped with the fleur-de-lys hallmark of Paris, while the goblet bears the "A M" mark of Amiens. Among these 14th-century objects are some of the oldest pieces known to bear the hallmark of the city in which they were made.

37

Showcase 29 contains another silver-gilt processional cross (37) decorated with translucent enamels and the figures of *Christ*, the *Virgin*, *St. John*, *St. Peter*, *Mary-Magdalen*, and, on the back, the *symbols of the Evangelists*, all standing out in high relief. It was executed in Central Italy around the second half of the 15th century and was once part of the famous collection of Prince Demidoff.

Showcase 30 displays various monstrances, that is, reliquaries usually fitted with a glass or crystal cylinder to permit the viewing of the relics. One of them, of Sienese craftsmanship, is decorated with translucent enamels and bears the date 1331. Two others were executed in Venice, one if the 14th century, and the other in the 15th: the base of the former is decorated with foliage in low relief, that of the second with the half-length figures of saints on a blue enamel ground.

In **Showcase 31** stands a fine silver-gilt *Virgin and Child*, the *reliquaries* of the navel of Christ (38). It is in the style of late 14th-century Parisian works.

Showcase 32 contains a variety of 14th and 15th-century objects, among which there is a vessel for Holy oil bearing the hallmark of Barcelona, and an arm-reliquary decorated with blue enamel rosettes.

Showcase 33 contains various reliquaries, including that of the foot of St. Alard, identified by an inscription in Italian. There is also a small cross, the base of a cross, and a large ostensory.

Showcase 34 also presents a variety of 15th-century objects: reliquaries, crosses, and censers.

37. Cross
38. Virgin and Child
39. St. Ann of the Trinity

Showcase 35 contains mostly examples of 15th-century German precious metalwork. In the middle stands the statue-reliquary of St. Anne (39); the "trinitarian" group of the saint holding the Virgin and Child is a typical motif in German iconography. A long inscription engraved on the back mentions that the work was executed in 1472 by Hans Greiff, an Ingolstadt goldsmith, for Anna Hofmann, the wife of the local tax-receiver.

Room **XVII**

Ceramics
Tiles

The variety in Medieval tiles is surprising, as can be seen from these two showcases displaying examples from the 13th to the 15th centuries. Some were stamped only with geometric or heraldic motifs (1), while others were also decorated with figurative scenes. Others were designed as elements of a composition. They come from different regions of the nothern part of France: the castille framed by a square set on end against a dark ground comes from the Château of Caen. The one with a design of four radiating fleur-de-lys comes from Saint-Denis. Several come from the Abbey of Fontenay.

Medieval pottery

So-called "flamulated" pottery (i.e., decorated only with strokes of red or black paint) was produced in a variety of forms for domestic use during the 12th and 13th centuries. Marks on the belly of some of them identify funerary vessels that were designed to hold burning embers and to be placed in tombs.

The glazed pottery (2) here was found in Paris during work in the boulevard Saint-Michel and the rue de la Harpe, and at Saint-Jean-de-Latran, rue des Grès. This type of pottery was a specialty of Paris from the 13th century onwards; green, yellow, and brown were used. The elaborate forms and relief effects indicate that these were a higher grade of wares.

In the top part of the showcase is displayed a magnificent serving dish decorated with the instruments of the Passion in relief, hence its name. It features an inscription with the date

1511, but the emblems belong to Charles VIII (†1498) and to his wife, Anne de Bretagne. In spite of this chronological discrepancy, its authenticity is no longer in doubt, for fragments of similar wares have been found at Beauvis. It is considered as one of the masterpieces of the Beauvais potters.

The large jar is a magnificent—and rare—example of glazed pottery from Spain.

Hispano-mauresque Pottery

The Musée de Cluny owns one of the leading collections of Spanish lusterware in the world. These fine pieces were produced at Manisès, in the outskirts of Valencia.

Many of the 15th-century wares exhibited here are of great rarity: in the middle of the cabinet are three deep bowls with "belières" (four bosses probably used to hang up the bowl); this is a unique set, for only one other such bowl in known to exist (in New York). The decoration in the Persian style, with eight-pointed stars (3), was modelled after 14th-century Andalusian wares; the color-scheme is a rich blend of almost purple blues and dark ocher tones. The two large pharmacy jars decorated in the same spirit, but with more muted blues, are from the first half of the 15th century. The same tones are to be seen in the *serving dish* and the *bowl* on either side, both decorated with a shield in the center and Arabic inscriptions; by comparison with a bowl in an American collection, they can be dated around 1430. The reverse side is decorated with a fierce and proud heraldic eagle framed by graceful plant motifs.

On the left of the cabinet are displayed some fine pieces with "ivy leaf" decoration: a serving dish and an ewer with these motifs in warm ocher tones, two *albarelli* with alternating blue and ocher leaves. One of the the major pieces of this collection is the large winged vase (4) on the belly of which is a shield with a lion that is said to be Florentine (a similar piece with the

1. *Pavement tile*
2. *Pitcher*
3. *Basin*

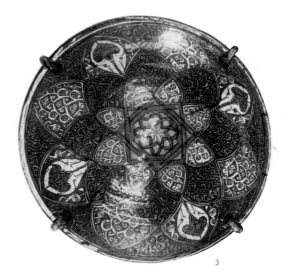

3

4. Winged vase

arms of the Medici is preserved in England). Grouped to the right on the cabinet and on the wall are a few pieces—serving dishes, bowl, a large cup—with delicate, blue "parsley leaf" motifs, one of the most attractive decorations conceived by the craftsmen of Manisès. Wares such as these were produced in large quantities between around 1430 and the end of the century.

Room XVIII

This room has been re-designed for the presentation of one of the Musée de Cluny's most important works: the complete set of choir stalls from the abbey of Saint-Lucien in Beauvais, which line three of the walls. The history of their acquisition, which is too involved to relate in detail here, can be summarized as follows: in 1820, the architect in charge of the restoration of the basilica of Saint-Denis acquired them and had them installed in the winter choir. They were partially dismantled in 1873 and placed in storage, before being assigned to the Musée de Cluny in 1889-1890. The first lot consisted only of two reveals (row-ends), a few pillars, and around forty seat frames and misericords. Two other lots have recently been added: one purchased in 1970, and another recovered from Saint-Denis to be dismantled and integrated into this reconstitution. The only modern elements are the base, the backs, and the arm-rests with their supports.

The two reveals displayed at the corner of the East and the North walls feature, on the North Side, the representation of *St. Peter Sending Saints Lucien, Maxien and Julien to Evangelize the Beauvais Region*, and, on the east side, the figure of *Antoine Du Bois*, the abbot who led them (1492-1500), *Kneeling before his Patron Saint*, the *Hermit Anthony* (1).

1. Choir stalls
from Saint-Lucien de Beauvais:
Antoine du Bois
Kneeling
before St. Anthony

The style of the misericords is not uniform, and this was taken into account for the reconstitution. Those on the North wall are the work of a sculptor who was influenced most likely by Northern art, for the subjects are complicated, the edges hard, and the folds angular. Those on the East wall, however, are the work of an artist with a different approach, for he depicted amusing scenes in a dignified manner. These misericords—a series illustrating different trades is exhibited in Room XXIII—are documents which give a vivid picture of life in the Middle Ages.

Displayed in the middle of the room on an octogonal stand are two Books of Hours, one from the beginning and the other from the middle of the 15th century. The margins are decorated with a filigree design, as was the practice at the time. The small scenes depicting the Labours of the Months are associated with the signs of the Zodiac, another Medieval custom (2).

On the South side is an important early 16th-century German altarpiece depicting scenes of the *Passion* carved in boxwood and set against a colored background. The side panels represent figures of *St. Accursius* and *St. Catherine*.

2. *Page from a Book of Hours: June/Cancer*

Room XIX

In this room adjacent to the Chapel have been assembled some of the Musée de Cluny's most precious pieces, an evocation of the rich treasures accumulated during the Middle Ages by the more important churches, examples of which can still be seen today at Conques, Sens, Aix-la-Chapelle (Aachen), San Marco in Venice, or at Monza, near Milan.

The Golden Altar of Basel

1. Complete
2. Detail

The Golden Altar of Basel.

The principal exhibit is the Golden Altar of Basel (1-2-3), the museum's rarest and most precious work. It was one of the many such "golden tables" that were placed before altars during the Carolingian and Ottonian periods (as in Byzantium), but most of them were melted down, such that today there are only four left in the world: the matchless "Paliotto" of S. Ambrogio of Milan, the "Pala d'Oro" of San Marco in Venice, the altar-front of the Cathedral of Aachen, and that of Basel, which became part of the museum's collections.

It is a masterpiece of the goldsmith's art: hammered gold leaf applied on a core of wood and wax. Framed by arcades and identified by inscriptions are the figures of *Christ blessing and holding the orb of the world—Rex regum et dominus dominantium—*, the three Archangels, *Michael*, *Gabriel* and *Raphael*, and *St. Benedict*, the first abbot of Monte Cassino and the founder of the order that bears his name. The background is decorated with luxuriant scroll motifs sourrounding four little medallions featuring bust-length figures of the Cardinal Virtues; the foliated ornamentation also fills the borders, twining around animal figures or putting forth leaves.

Recent research tends to indicate that the "altar" was made in the second or beginning of the third decade of the 11th century by Germanic goldsmiths (of Fulda, where some contemporary frescoes suggest more or less conclusive comparisons), at the request of Emperor Henry II, called the "Holy" or the "Lame", who had himself represented along with his wife, the Empress Cunégonde, kneeling at the feet of Christ. It is thought to have been destined for a Benedictine monastery—perhaps even Monte Cassino—, which would explain the choice of figures represented. But the emperor, pressed by financial difficulties or motivated by political considerations, may have decided to give it to the city of Basel instead. With the outbreak of religious conflicts in the 16th century, it was hidden for safekeeping beneath the cathedral. It was sold in 1836 by the Canton of Basel along with part of the Treasury, and came into the Musée de Cluny's collections in 1854.

3. The Golden Altar of Basel (detail)

The Ivories

A large showcase assembles the more ancient ivories in the museum's collections, as well as a few equally valuable pieces of precious metalwork and small sculptures.

First bay (on the left).

On the left, a large figure carved in ivory—one of the largest ever made in this material—representing *Ariadne* (4), possibly a furniture decoration which may have been matched by a Dionysios; she is standing, holding a thyrsus and a cup, surrounded by two cupids and a satyr. The refinement of this group, with its supple style and flowing draperies, suggests that it was executed in Constantinople around the year 500 or in the early 6th century. In the middle are displayed three plaquettes: the one which represents *Christ Crowning the Germanic Emperor Otto II (972-983) and His Wife the Byzantine Princess Theophano* (5), was probably the work of an artist from Byzantium established in the West (rather than the "Western imitation" of a Byzantine ivory, as some have suggested). As for the figure of a saint in prayer, it may well be one of the rare examples of a Near-Eastern Christian ivory from the Umayyad period (7th-8th centuries). The last plaquette, which depicts the Dormition of the Virgin, is a work of the Mid-Byzantine Period (10th-11th centuries). On the right, the leaf of the diptych of Areobindus (6) (appointed Consul in Constantinople in 506) is an example of the custom, reserved for high officials, of addressing ivory diptychs to their friends as invitations to the games that they offered to celebrate their accession to office. Here, the consul bears the insignia of his rank and holds, in his right hand, the *mappa*, a handkerchief that was thrown as a starting signal for the games (represented below).

Beneath this piece is displayed a portable altar with a porphyry plaque, gold and silver mounts, and ivory reliefs, it is a German work of the 12th century. Next to it is a pyxis from late Antiquity, probably of Eastern Mediterranean origin and dating from the 5th-6th centuries; it features scenes of the Miracles of Christ.

4. Ariadne
5. Christ
Crowning Otto II
and Theophano
6. Panel from the Diptych
of Areobindus

5

4   6

7

Second bay

In the middle is displayed one of the masterpieces of late Romanesque art, clearly of Classical inspiration: one of the panels of a diptych intended probably to commemorate a marriage between two families of illustrious senators (the Nicomachi and the Symmachi), around the year 400 (7); the second panel is in the Victoria and Albert Museum in London. In the Middle Ages, the two panels were remounted in a reliquary at the abbey church of Montier-en-Der (Haute-Marne). The panel here was found hidden in a well, which explains its damaged condition; according to the attributes represented, it shows a priestess of Ceres near an altar consecrated to Cybele.

To the left of this singular piece stands a remarkable *Crucifixion* carved in wood with a beautiful brown patina, a 12th-century German work and a small schist icon of the 11th-13th century, depicting two *Soldier Saints Receiving from Christ the Crowns* (formerly painted on the background) *of their Martyrdom*. On the right, notice two lead plaques with figures of *Apostles* or *Prophets*, works of very high quality whose classicizing style permits a dating around the beginning of the 5th century.

At the bottom may be seen another Paleochristian pyxis from the Near-East (depicting the *Healing of a Person Blind from Birth*), a precious 13th-century bookbinding (8) incorporating Byzantine or Byzantine-inspired ivories on the back, and, on the cover, a Carolingian *Crucifixion* (in the style of the "Second Lotharingian School"), and, lastly, a portable altar with an "antique green" porphyry plaque (9): on the engraved silver and partially-gilded leaves that enclose it, it features, besides the inscription along the edge, the figures of the *Christ in Glory, Saints Peter, Paul, Blaise*, and *Nicholas*, then *Aaron and Melchizedech*, and the *Sacrifice of Abraham* (above), and the *Mystic Lamb* and the *Four Cardinal Virtues* (below); stylistically and iconographically, this work is related to the Basel "altar" and must have had the same origins (German Empire—perhaps Fulda—, first half of the 11th century).

7. Panel from the Diptych
of the Symmachi and Nicomachi
8. Binding
9. Portable altar

On the right wall, the rather worn figure of *St. Paul* belongs to a group of works which very probably originated in the Eastern Mediterranean during the 6th-7th centuries, although some have argued for a Gallic origin (the Latin inscription could very well have been added at a later date).

Third bay

The figure of an apostle in the Carolingian style and two plaques that demonstrate the diversity of works produced in the Ottonian Empire around the year 1000: a *Crucifixion* from Cologne (10) (which shows the Christ, clad in a long, windblown tunic that twists in a remarkable movement), and a *St. Paul* executed in Echternach (12) whose strong relief and powerful features seem to anticipate the renewal of the monumental style. Displayed below are two panels of a re-used diptych (11): on the back of each can still be seen some Christian motifs, probably carved in an Anglo-Saxon workshop around the 8th century, and later planed down; on the front, some 10th-century artists (North Italian?) carved various figures and creatures from the repertoire of classical mythology in a decor of foliated scrolls, very likely inspired by the "Etymologies" of Isidor of Seville, which were widely glossed during the Carolingian period.

Liturgical Vestments

This showcase displays a few rare liturgical vestments and some ivories; on the left, the crozier of St. Martin. The Romanesque ivory volute depicting the *Adoration of the Magi* was mounted in the 13th century on a boxwood staff decorated with thirty scenes illustrating the *Life of Christ*. Notice the four caskets, the first of which is Byzantine from the 10th-11th centuries, the second, undecorated, of French workmanship from the 14th century, the third executed by Arab craftsmen working in Sicily, and the last—the casket-reliquary of St. Yved de Braine—with figures represented under arcades on gilded plaquettes, was made in Cologne around the year 1200.

In the center of the showcase is the silk tunic found in the tomb of Pierre de Courpalay (†1334) at Saint-Germain-des-Prés; on either side are two velvet chasubles onto which older embroideries were sewn. To the right is a magnificent early 15th-century *Crucifixion* on a blue background, surmounted by a figure of the *Virgin Fainting*. To the left is an early 16th-century *Crucifixion* featuring *St. John* and the *Virgin* in the lower part (13).

The bishop's stocking of green silk decorated with gazelles and birds was found in the tomb of Arnaud de Via (†1355). The Luccan craftsman who wove it took care to enliven it with gold thread. The precious bishop's glove also comes from the tomb of Pierre de Courpalay.

The magnificient Cufic inscription in long blue letters was found in the tomb of a bishop of Bayonne.

The "horn of the unicorn" is in fact the tusk of a narwhal, a type of whale which lives in Arctic waters and whose teeth form this curious growth. In the Middle Ages it was thought to possess miraculous powers and so was preciously preserved. This one comes from the Treasury of Saint-Denis.

10. Crucifixion
11. Diptych panel:
figures and animals
in foliage motif
12. St. Paul
13. Chasuble

13

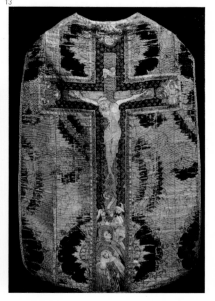

12

Room **XX**

2

The Chapel

Built above a vaulted passage that connects one of the courtyards of the Thermae to the Gothic gardens, the Chapel is one of the most elegant remaining examples of late Medieval architecture. The usual exuberance of the Flamboyant style is tempered here by an exquisite sense of moderation, flawless proportions, and tasteful ornamentation, making of this little oratory a truly perfect architectural achievement.

It has suffered little from the passage of time: the twelve statues representing different members of the d'Amboise family disappeared during the Revolution, but the virtuosity of the sculptors may still be admired in the corbels decorated with vines and oak branches, and the finely-carved canopies. Below, twelve consecration crosses painted, according to ecclesiastical custom, at the time of the consecration. An intricate network of lierne patterns fills the vault surfaces, or at least the spaces left between the profusion of ribs fanning out from the slender load-bearing pillar standing in the center of the room. The suspended keystones at the intersection of the arches have unfortunately been lost. The small apse to the east, which corbels out on a pillar outside, formerly housed the altar; the aperture in the buttress on the right permitted the abbot to observe the priest from the adjacent room, and thus to follow the services without leaving his well-heated quarters. Some 15th-century sculptures are still visible on the vault of this apse: *God the Father Blessing*, *Christ on the Cross*, angels flying or carrying the instruments of the Passion. The contribution of the Renaissance to the decoration of this oratory are the mural paintings, on either side of the altar, representing *Mary Salome* and *Mary Jacobi* lamenting the tragedy of the *Crucifixion*. In one of the corners of the chapel is a small, descending spiral staircase dissimulated behind a curved stone screen whose large, flowing tracery gracefully adorns this side of the room.

To bring out the sacred character of this edifice—in the absence of an altar—we have installed in the apse an altar front representing four holy personages under large arcades: a bishop, a martyred deacon, *St. Peter*, and *St. Jerome*; this fine work was found during the construction of the rue des Écoles, that is to say on the very land owned by the Cluny abbots at the time of the building of their *hôtel*. On the altar thus improvised has been placed a gilt and silvered cross, a vestige of the *église des Grands Carmes* which formerly stood on the nearby place Maubert.

The baptismal font is a 14th-century work from the church of Embsen in Hanover (1).

Against the North wall is the funeral effigy of Blanche de Champagne (†1283) (2), the wife of Jean I, Duke of Brittany, which comes from the abbey of La Joie, near Hennebont (Morbihan); it is composed of a roughly-carved wooden core covered with sheets of brass.

1. Baptismal font from Embsen
2. Funerary
statue of Blanche de Champagne
(detail)

The Legend of St. Stephen

The History and Legend of St. Stephen is one of the most famous Gothic tapestry sets in the museum's collections. Its warm blues, greens, and luminous reds are a perfect complement to these somewhat cold expanses of stone, and at the same time, this chapel provides a perfect setting, for they are in fact "choir hangings", tapestries of a type often used in the Middle Ages to decorate the sanctuaries of important churches. This set was commissioned around 1490 by the bishop of Auxerre, Jean Baillet, and for the next three hundred years, it decorated the choir of the Auxerre cathedral; it was put up for sale at the end of the 18th century, and again in 1880, before being acquired in its entirety by the Musée de Cluny. It is 45 meters long and has been hung in the Chapel and in two of the adjacent rooms. The subject is the story of St. Stephen, the patron saint of Auxerre,

and of the invention of his relics, depicted in a sequence of 23 tableaux. The first episodes are exhibited in the Chapel (starting on the back wall), the continuation in Room XIX, and the end in Room XVIII. Visitors will thus be able to follow, scene by scene, one of the typical "Lives of the Saints" popularized by works such as Jacopo de Voragine's *Golden Legend* (13th century) which sustained the impassioned and somewhat gullible faith of Medieval worshippers.

Tapestries of St. Stephen

Scene 8
1. *Complete*
2. *Detail*
3. *Scene 9 (detail)*
4. *Scene 2 (detail)*

Room XX

Room XIX

West Wall

1. A council of the apostles decides to appoint seven deacons to settle disputes between the first Christians.
2. St. Peter consecrating St. Stephen and his companions by the imposition of his hands (4).

North Wall

3. Inspired by the Holy Spirit, St. Stephen discusses with the Jewish doctors.
4. St. Stephen is summoned to appear before the court of the High Priest and is accused of blasphemy by false witnesses.
5. In front of the scandalized Jews, St. Stephen claims that he sees Christ in Heaven, seated at the right-hand side of the Lord.

South Wall

6. St. Stephen is mistreated and dragged out of the city.
7. Praying for his enemies, St. Stephen is stoned to death, while the young Saul watches over the executioners' clothes.

South Wall

8. The martyr's soul rises to heaven and wild beasts stand watch over his remains (1-2).
9. Gamaliel secretly lays the body of St. Stephen in his own tomb (3).

West Wall

10. Four centuries later, Gamaliel appears three times in the dreams of the priest Lucian, touching him with a golden rod and showing him four baskets filled with flowers, symbols of the bodies to be discovered.

11. Reporting his vision to the bishop of Jerusalem, Lucian reveals the will of God.

Corner Wall

12. In the presence of a great number of clergymen, the bishop of Jerusalem tries to find the martyr's tomb, without success.

North Wall

13. The monk Migetius, to whom Gamaliel had also appeared, reveals the location of the sepulcher.

14. The transfer of the relics to Jerusalem is accompanied by many miracles.

Room XVIII

West Wall

15. The widow of a Greek senator, sending heralds with letters from the emperor, asks permission for the transfer of her husband's body from St. Stephen's oratory in Jerusalem to Constantinople.

16. The body of St. Stephen is shipped by mistake and the saint appears to the passengers to save them from the storm and from demons.

17. The body of St. Stephen is greeted with honors by the Byzantine clergy.

North Wall

18. The emperor of Constantinople orders the reliquary casket of the saint to be brought to his palace, but the mules, stopped by an angel, refuse to advance (5-6).

East Wall

19. In Rome, Eudoxia, possessed by demons, reveals the will of God, and her father, the emperor Theodosius, has the Pope request that the body of St. Stephen be exchanged for the body of St. Lawrence.

Tapestries of St. Stephen

Scene 18
5. *Complete*
6. *Detail*

20. Arrived from Constantinople, the body of St. Stephen is solemnly received by the Pope, who has it placed in the church of S. Pietro-in-Vincoli.
21. From the mouth of Eudoxia, the demon reveals that the body of St. Stephen, must rest by the side of St. Lawrence.
22. The envoys from Constantinople fall as if struck dead when they try to take the body of St. Lawrence.
23. St. Lawrence makes roon in his sepulcher for the body of St. Stephen; the demon flies out of the mouth of Eudoxia, and the angels in Heaven sing, all for the greater glory of the city of Rome.

Room XXI

In this room have been grouped some particularly important works, such as the Stavelot Altarpiece, displayed on the East wall (1-2).

Acquired at Koblenz during the Revolutionary Wars, it comes from the Abbey of Stavelot in Belgium and was executed shortly after the middle of the 12th century. Like most of the large shrines (*châsse*) of Rhenish-Mosan origin, it contains few enamelled parts: only the nimbuses, which may have been added later, and the arch from which emerges the bust of Christ were decorated with enamels. The gilt-brass figures done in repoussé work are close to those of the *châsse* of St. Héribert at Deutz.

Nearby is a magnificent lectern in the form of an eagle from the church of St. Nicholas at Tournai (3). Along the base runs an inscription which tells us that it was donated in 1383 by two wool merchants, Damians and Velaine. On the same side there is a gilt-brass and painted *Crucifixion* which features on the back the "huchette" emblem of Antoine, "*grand bâtard*" of Burgundy. On the north wall (garden side) hangs a painted triptych from Flanders: The side-panels represent the donor and his family being presented by St. John the Bapstist and a female saint, while the center panel depicts the *Miraculous Mass of St. Gregory*. Displayed above

some 14th-century choir stalls on the West wall, are two large fragments of a tapestry series on the *Life of the Virgin*, donated in memory of Jacques Bary by Mmes Pauline and Clotilde Bari (4). The presence, on the left, of Léon Conseil, Chancellor of the church of Bayeux, accompanied by an abbot and their patron saints, St. Exupère and St. Paul, permits us to identify this as part of the tapestries offered by this dignitary to the Cathedral of Bayeux in 1499. On the right are three scenes: the *Annunciation*, the *Visitation*, and *the Virgin and St. Joseph in a Interior*.

On the South wall (courtyard side) there is a panel reprensenting *Lazarus and the Rich Man* painted by a Parisian artist around the 1420's (5).

The Stavelot Altarpiece

1. Complete
2. Detail

4

3

3. *Lectern*
4. *Scenes from the Life
of the Virgin*
5. *Lazarus
and the Miser*

5

6

staff—with a very "Romanesque" stylization of the plant motifs—, said to have been found in the tomb of Abbot Morard of Saint-Germain-des-Prés (around the year 1000), the rustic crozier from Villeloin, and the mysterious little "monument" in the shape of a church with several Christian subjects, including an *Adoration of the Magi.*

A showcase in the middle of the room contains a few painted enamels considered to be among the "incunabula" of a technique that was to have a wide success during the 16th century. It had been a specialty of Limoges as early as the middle of the 15th century, and consisted in the use of especially pre-

In the Northeast corner of the room stands a display case which contains some of the more rare pre-Romanesque and Romanesque ivories in the museum's collections. Among these are forty whalebone plaquettes that formerly decorated a Mozarabic casket (North of the Iberian peninsula, 2nd half on the 10th century); the elements with Christian figural scenes (including a *Christ in Majesty* (6) and the *Suicide of Judas*) alternated in an unknown order with elements featuring animal or plant motifs, separated by borders with eyelet (ocelle) designs, the whole treated in the same flat and schematic style as the contemporary illuminations produced in this particular artistic environment. The two oliphants (7) (elephant-tusk horns) and the bookbinding plaques representing the Christ and various saints were most likely made in the 10th century in the South of Italy, which at the time was the focal point of Byzantine and Islamic influences in the West. Of purely Anglo-Saxon origin is the plaquette (from a casket?) with a very delicate openwork decoration of scrolls and animal protomes (first half of the 11th century), while the fine walrus-tusk ivory crozier (8) which also features zoomorphic and plant motifs already shows the effects of the Norman conquest of England. Of French fabrication are the pastoral "Tau"

7

8

6. *Christ*
in Majesty
7. *Oliphant*
8. *Crozier*

pared copper plaques onto which different layers of colored enamel were applied. Tentatively at first, during the last third of the 15th century, the techniques were to undergo profound modifications starting in the 1520's. Before this date the Limousin enamellers maintained the Gothic tradition. The name of Monvaerni has been given to one of their oldest craftsmen, to whom is attributed a *Virgin of the Pity* between two donors. The Pénicaud family carried enamelling techniques to their highest levels; Nardon executed the beautiful *Crucifixion* dated 1504; and Jean, the *Road to Calvary* and another *Crucifixion*.

Room XXII

Metalwork — Arms

Given the importance that iron has had in all civilizations, it seemed only fitting to devote a room to it in a museum of the Middle Ages. Because of its ductility and malleability in its natural state, this metal lends itself to any number of uses and shapes, and it has the added advantage of being easily welded together, provided that the oxidized coating created by the fire is removed. It can be shaped by repeated heating and hammering, and decorated by stamping (with a die, while hot) or by filing.

One of the Medieval ironsmiths' most original contributions was their wrought-iron work. In the flat showcase in front of the window are a few stamped fragments from one of the doors of Notre-Dame (early 13th century). Nearby, a contemporary door brace has been mounted on a wood panel. The imagination of the craftsmen had its freest scope in the decoration of grilles, which lent themselves to the most fanciful designs. Displayed are two magnificent 12th-century grilles from Saint-Denis (1), and some others ranging in date from the 13th to the 15th centuries.

In a fireplace which has the same provenance as the *Vie Seigneuriale* tapestries, are displayed a Medieval fireback bearing the royal coat-of-arms, two andirons, a pot-hook, a grill, and a meat-hanger.

A "mille-fleurs" tapestry hanging above a chest illustrates the art of forging, represented by Tubalcain, its legendary founder, and the art of weighing.

2

1. *Grille*
2. *Chest*
3. *Mold for Holy wafers*
4. *Bolt*

1

4

Some of the objects exhibited in the middle are particularly interesting: the chest on legs covered with metal plates held in place by stamped straps (14th century) (2); the two large church chandeliers; a folding desk; and, especially, some molds for sacramental wafers (14th, 15th, 16th centuries). The finest ones, of circular shape, are engraved on one side with the *Christ Blessing*, surrounded by scenes of his Life, and on the other, with the *Christ Showing His Wounds* among figures of the twelve apostles (3).

3

Showcase 1: *locks*

The large collection of locks and bolts from the late Middle Ages show how the Flamboyant style invaded all types of production. Even the hasps that hid the keyholes were decorated with figures. The inscription IHS may be seen on a very fine 15th-century bolt (4). Next to it is a no-less remarkable lock for a chest.

Keys

The display-case in front of the window shows the evolution of keys from the Roman period until the beginning of the 16th century as well as the different types in use: with a lifting action, full rotation, or an angular displacement.

Knives

A small showcase contains a variety of knives, including a 14th-century hunting knife, two magnificent meat-carving knives with a curved blade. The rarest item is the knife with a handle chased and enamelled with the arms of Philip the Good, Duke of Burgundy.

Arms and armor

The struggle for life, with the warfare that it entails, has dominated the history of man ever since its beginnings. To supplement the action of his own arms, and also to protect them, man has used every kind of material: at first wood and stone, then bronze, iron and steel, whose flexibility lent itself to· his many requirements. The Middle Ages marked a significant step with the appearance of armor for the foot soldier and, most importantly, for the horseman. His armament will evolve over time, but slowly because of the cost of fabrication. Although produced in great quantity, most of the armor has been lost, due to the effects of war, time, rust, and... fashion. In order to learn about arms and armor, it is necessary to consult illustrated material, which fortunately is very abundant.

Showcase 3

In spite of the richness and diversity of its collections, for a long time the museum did not possess any armor, except for the beaked helmet (*mézail de bacinet* (5) which is displayed at the bottom center of the showcase; the pointed visor helped the blows to glance off, but the eye-slits seem too large to afford much protection. This piece was acquired only in 1909, after having been in the collections of Carrand and Victor Gay; it is said to have been found at Azincourt, the site of a famous battle of 1415, and indeed seems to be contemporary with this event.

Five helmets have obligingly been lent by the Musée de l'Armée, whose important collections are preserved at the Invalides, as well as other helmets of different types, greaves, and gauntlets.

Showcase 4, recess of middle window.

Displayed are two interesting, though incomplete, examples of brigandines, a sort of protective garment composed of blades of steel riveted together so as to overlap and covered with velvet material fastened by nails that were usually gilded. The one on the left is a breast-piece which still has the fabric covering fixed onto the armor; only the metal blades of the other one, probably a back-piece, remain, showing the variety and the subtlety of the forms. In between them is an early 16th-century Italian gauntlet.

Showcase 5

On the left, two Viking swords dating from before or just after their settlement in Normandy in the 10th century, and an 11th-century Norman sword of the kind used at the time of the conquest of England (1066) and which can be seen in the famous Bayeux Tapestry.

5

6

On the right, three elegant 15th-century swords from the magnificent collection bequeathed by Count Edouard de Beaumont in 1888. One of them features the serpent emblem of the Sforzas of Milan; another, probably German, was intended to be attached to the saddlebow.

In the middle, various arms: a mace and a war hammer, both from the 15th century; a *"broqhel"*, or small, round shield for foot soldiers. In the middle another German sword from the collection of E. de Beaumont (2nd half of the 15th cent.); in the 16th century, an engraved and gilt decoration was added to the blade to fix a dynastic tradition: on one side, a German inscription which reads, "Tournament sword of the Emperor Frederick, in the year of our Lord 1459"; on the other, a portrait of this same emperor, Frederick III, the father-in-law of Mary of Burgundy.

On the floor, a large sword with a curved blade, known as a "falchion" and used by foot soldiers; this one is from the 13th century and its bronze pommel features an engraved and enamelled heraldic "castille". It was found in 1861 during excavations near the Pont-au-Change.

Showcase 6, opposite the preceding one.

In addition to locks, the locksmiths also made boxes and caskets, either entirely of metal, or in wood that could be covered either with leather or with parchment banded with metal. The steel parts could be decorated with molding, stamped designs, or cut-out shapes.

Most of these caskets are so close in style and form that one could suppose that they were made in the same place. The slightly-domed lids, the heavy molding, the openwork plaques, the Flamboyant tracery designs around the lock, are all characteristic of the 15th century, and particularly the end of this century. Compare their style to that of certain door fastenings from the hospice of Beaune (2nd half of the 15th cent).

Displayed on the East wall is a large collection of targes (small, round bucklers) and *"pavois"*, wooden shields covered with leather or cloth (6). They come from Central Europe: Germany, Bohemia. Some are of remarkably fine quality, such as the one decorated with the figures of *David and Goliath* in the center.

5. *Helmet with beaked visor*
6. *Shield*

Cy sont les representations et nobles persones messire Jehan juuenal des ursins cheualier Samour et huun de juuenal Conseillier du roy. Et madame sa file de vitry sa femme, et de leurs enfans.

In the middle, a long painting on a wood panel representing the Jouvenal des Ursins family (7): Jean Jouvenal (†1431), Provost of the traders of Paris, his wife Jeanne de Vitry, and their eleven children. It was executed between 1445 and 1449 by a Parisian artist for the chapel of Saint-Rémy at Notre-Dame.

7. *The Family*
of Jouvenal des Ursins
8. *Measure*
for the tithe

Below, two bombards and a 14th-century culverin, examples of the firearms which came into use at the end of the Middle Ages. Nearby, a wooden statue of *St. George* outfitted in a typical 15th-Century suit of armor.

8

Room **XXIII**

In this room have been assembled primarily works made of copper alloys, such as brass and bronze. Because it is so easy to extract and work, copper has long played an important rôle in all civilizations. Low in density, ductile and malleable, it is usually combined with other metals: mixed with tin and zinc, it becomes bronze, and mixed with zinc alone, it makes brass (the latter was a specialty of the town of Dinant, in Belgium, hence the term "Dinanderie", which has become synonymous with brassware).

1. Aquamanile

On the West wall, the first showcase (left) presents elements of caskets and reliquaries, as well as a few candlesticks, most with figural designs, and a "Pax" date 1468. Some of these objects are worthy of closer attention: for instance, the 12th-century crucifix whose fine green patina is the result of a long time spent underground, and a colonnette from a casket, also of the 12th century. The second showcase contains many everyday objects: chandelier, ewers, and aquamaniles; the latter, the oldest of which date from the 12th century, were often fashioned in the shape of fantastic animals, such as the griffin and the unicorn here (1). The third showcase presents, apart from a 15th-century Flemish *Virgin and*

Child, works from the West and from the Paleochristian or Medieval Near-East; among the latter may be noted three censers and a lamp base decorated with claws, a characteristic feature of ecclesiastical furniture of the 5th-7th centuries. Displayed on the same side, on the upper part of the wall, are some 16th-century brass alms-plates.

2. *Chalice*
3. *Pilgrim's bottle*

Pewter and lead also were often used in the Middle Ages. Being malleable and of low cost, they were used for the fabrication of everyday ustensils. Because of their fragility, however, not many of these objects have come down to us. The showcase on the North wall contains only objects made of pewter. The absolution cross found in a tomb and bearing an inscription in the name of one Edelbert, who died at Archiac during the reign of Philip I, is a unique piece. The 12th-century chalice (2) is no less rare. The 13th-century vial found in the Seine (3) was used by pilgrims to hold holy water or oil. The 14th-century salt featuring an *Annunciation* (4) scene is close to a similar object preserved at the Kunstgewerbe Museum in Berlin. Many of the open-work plaques were used in the fabrication of caskets. As for the small rounded or sealed cups, of which the museum has a large collection, no one knows what purpose they served.

5

4

The majority of the objects displayed in the showcase on the East wall come from the Gay and Forgeais collections, which were assembled in the wake of the dredging operations effected in the Seine between 1848 and 1860. They consist of pilgrims' badges, which were bought at pilgrimage sites and worn pinned to clothing and hats. Most of the great shrines of France (Le Puy, Boulogne, Mont Saint-Michel) are evoked by these small figurines, some of which were executed with great skill (5-6-7).

4. Salt-cellar
5. Pilgrimage badge:
St. George
6. Pilgrimage badge:
Saint-Maur-des-Fossés

6

*8. Comb
of Marguerite
de Flandre*

In front of the window on the South wall are displayed a few molds, some of which were used for metals. The round slate mold (German, 15th century) is a masterpiece in itself, but its function remains a mystery.

The other showcase on this side presents a collection of boxwood combs; the most remarkable of these, which features marquetry and bone inlays (elements of which were colored in green), bears on both faces a silver plaque with the monogram and coat-of-arms of Margaret of Flanders (†1405), the wife of Philip the Bold.

In the middle of the room stands a baptismal font made of lead.

Also displayed, along with a few misericords from the choir stalls of Saint-Lucien of Beauvais decorated with crafts motifs, is a small tapestry panel bearing the emblem of the Robertet family, famous for its lawyers and financiers.

*7. Pilgrimage badge:
Notre-Dame de Rocamadour*

*9. Medallion:
Crowned
female head*

9

7

This book
was printed
on the presses
of the Imprimerie Mame
in Tours
in February 1987.

Designed
by Joël Cuénot.

Text set in Caslon
by Union Linotypiste.
Plates
engraved by Point 11.
Paper manufactured
at the Job
paper mills.

All photography provided by:
Réunion
des musées nationaux.

Dépôt légal :
1er trimestre 1987

ISBN : 2-7118-2.070-X
(French edition, RMN, 1986).

ISBN : 2-7118-2.071-8
(English edition, RMN).

8021-012